The Dandelion Diary

The tricky art of walking

The Dandelion Diary

The tricky art of walking

MARGUERITE BLACK

HUMAN & ROUSSEAU

Cape Town Pretoria

Marguerite Black: cmblack@mweb.co.za

Copyright © 2006 by Marguerite Black

First published in 2006 by Human & Rousseau,

a division of NB Publishers (Pty) Limited,

40 Heerengracht, Cape Town, 8001 (Head office)

1064 Arcadia Street, Pretoria, 0083

Photograph on cover: Lisa Myburgh

Cover and page design by Chérie Collins

Set in 11 on 16 pt Minion

Printed and bound by Paarl Print, Oosterland Street, Paarl, South Africa

ISBN-10 0-7981-4631-1

ISBN-13 978-0-7981-4631-9

For my mother

"Slide the weight from your shoulders and move forward. You are afraid you might forget, but you never will. You will forgive and remember . . . move on. Walk forward into the light."

BARBARA KINGSOLVER, *The Poisonwood Bible*

"I can understand the nature of the living being
outside of myself only through the living being
within me . . ."

ALBERT SCHWEITZER

The weaver

I spin stories for you,
in you,
like a cocoon,
a pocket in which you can live,
cushioning you from sharpness,
sudden impact.

I spin stories for you,
unfolding them before you
like a Persian rug
which I weave with thought,
laced with laughter, on which you can tiptoe
through the paths of your life.

Dancing in the garden

The flight of the thistledown

I started to dance a while ago, in my own way. I began to think back, remembering a time when I could move freely, like wind breathing through ferns in a forest. And for quite a while now, as my movements became increasingly difficult, I have been tracing the events, people and thoughts that have shaped me through these desperate and wondrous years.

It was only twenty years ago – a morning filled with noisy, laughing children:

I am eight years old and thrilled to be part of the activity on a sports field in Grahamstown that has been going on since early in the morning. It is the annual sports day of the school and the excitement and anticipation can be felt in the air. Mothers rush around in the biting cold of the dawn putting up tents and stalls to protect their children from the sweltering heat which will surely surface later in the day. The Eastern Cape has been described as "a region of fierce opposites – meadows and plains, dongas and waterfalls, ferns and aloes". Of Grahamstown it is said that there are four seasons in one day. In an attempt to reconcile these opposites, the children sit on the stands in shorts with warmer tracksuits packed into bags by their sides. Among the children I sit, and jump up impulsively when the under nines' 100m is announced over the microphone.

The gun goes off and I throw my legs forward with exaggeration and gusto. I can feel my body bursting with vitality as the blood rushes through my limbs. Determination and focus allow me to win the race. After the thrill of the moment, the applause subsides and I casually walk off towards the hotdog stand.

At this moment I am unaware of the fact that in the near future I might not have the freedom to amble nonchalantly towards a hotdog stand, absent-mindedly glancing towards the sky and constructing patterns in the clouds. I do not foresee the way in which I will soon have to use my determination and focus. And it will not be for furthering my athletic abilities. It will be for something of a devastatingly different kind – in fact, a fierce opposite.

I was soon to embark on a journey where every step in itself would be a race, and where, whenever in motion, it would be dangerous to be absent-minded for one second. Because that would mean that I could fall and hurt myself.

The regimented order of a day on the sports field wasn't a patch on a day spent in our garden, which was like a jungle to me. Here, my feet could take me wherever I wished to go. It was 1985, languid days of roaming around and discovering a small green worm, dragging itself along in the dust, or a light blue snake-egg, strange and brittle. I often think back to and long for those days, when I could run freely and when my legs would listen to me and carry me even to the impossible places that my little-girl imagination demanded of me: up a steep tree to scrutinise a leaf or down a flight of steps in a flurry. I was blissfully unaware of what the future held. Now I know the future's unpredictability is a privilege. When I was a child the mountain could always come to me, I could sing with the cicadas and fly up high with the swallows.

The garden

Loquats
half-maimed,
eaten by mousebirds,
the jungle of a child,
mtwana of the veld.
Here bird funerals
were held
and feasts of prickly pears.
Abakweta-shongololos
were the scarecrows of the plains.

Here warm berg winds
rustled through summer grass.
Goats on the hill
grazed amongst kikuyu.
Here geckos were our snakes
and Datsuns racing cars.
Garden of trampled dandelions,
the jungle of a child.

My brother, Malcolm, and I spent every possible moment after school in gangs made up of the children from the neighbourhood. Down by the dam and up by the railway line on the hill, we conducted funerals for birds with a designated priest and casket carriers, or relentlessly dug unsuccessful swimming pools in the earth during the ruthless heat of summer. Every morning the hill, a mass of rampant natural growth that could not easily be tamed by humans, would slowly

Playing in the garden

come alive with cattle herders, now whistling, now talking in low monotones.

On such a day I went to one of my friends' birthday parties a few blocks away. I ran through the long grass in the field behind our house, the heady fragrance of kukumakranka fruits in the air. From somewhere close by, I could hear the hissing and rapid honking of an Egyptian goose before flight. On arrival, the tune of "Oranges and Lemons" was intermingling with bright balloons bobbing up and down. In the corner of my eye, at the foot of the stairs leading up to their house, I could see an older girl in a wheelchair. Instantly my eyes moved, fixing on her for an immeasurable fragment of time. Confusion took hold of me: I had always thought that walking was everyone's birthright, not to mention a necessity for survival. It was cruel to deny anyone proper legs. How could anyone carry such a burden? The excited shrieks of the children grew suddenly muffled and remote as a faint sense of familiarity rippled through me and swelled into a wave of recognition. A strange feeling that I had never sensed before tugged at my gut and somehow, in that moment, I felt completely disconnected from myself. But then the ring-a-ring-a-rosies children called out to me to come and hold hands with them and complete the circle. Feeling out of sorts, I reluctantly ran towards the splash of colour in the garden.

After the party, immersed in the day's last shafts of sunlight, I ran down the hill to our sprawling house. It seemed determined to stand its ground in this harsh landscape. It was a Fifties-style home sandwiched between two hills and cloistered behind fussy white burglar bars that made twists and twirls, reminding me of decorations on a wedding cake. There was a terraced lawn spread out in front of the house and in the flowerbeds was a tangle of petunias, daffodils and geraniums. In fact, just about every conceivable garden flower that was able to withstand the extreme climatic changes had been planted haphazardly, so that I could imagine the lawn being inundated by dandelions and inhabited by all sorts of bush creatures. The piping of a bearded robin echoed across the garden, jolting me out of my sombre mood and catapulting me into a buoyant lightness. I looked up and saw the coppery sheen of a few hadedas, taking leave, in their rasping kind of way, of the wilting sun.

The pewter jewellery box

Inside, the house was a strange mixture of stylistic elements – an eclectic goulash, I now realise. There were kelims from Istanbul, Delft porcelain from Holland, yellowwood furniture from second-hand shops and Indian sari's used as throws on the sofas and for a table cloth on the dining room table. I could see a cuckoo peeking out of its Austrian clock in one of the rooms and Belgian beer jugs aligned on a shelf in the kitchen. A dresser housed an entire extended family of babushkas. There were so many, in fact, that each one's alter ego or imaginary playmate probably accompanied it. And a whole array of African masks from the Ivory Coast adorned the walls. The concept of minimalism wasn't very high on our list of priorities.

That afternoon there were freshly picked flowers on the windowsills, but there was also an acrid smell of burnt dough in the house. My mother flurried out onto the porch in a flowing dress. She looked startled at the Jerusalem thorn tree enshrouded by the darkening dusk in the front garden and said: "When did the night gobble up the day? Was I in never-never land? Sweets, your mother is losing it . . . I can't seem to bake biscuits for my own children! What will become of you, my dear Gita?"

Both my parents had an array of nicknames for me. This one made me feel glowing and special.

Sharing a joke with my mom

We went into the kitchen. My mother had been baking sugar biscuits. She had cut the dough into funny flower shapes, moon shapes in various lunar phases and terrifying sun shapes and had decorated the biscuits with pink, yellow and baby blue icing, covering them with little silver balls and colourful sprinkles. As we walked past, she exclaimed: "Sherbet! These biscuits are just for looking at!"

The next moment, a bunch of keys was clattering noisily in the door and my dad, with his untidy beard and ethnic beads dangling round his neck, was making his way towards the table, a whiff of pencil shavings and sweat coming from his clothes. He hurriedly put his faded leather briefcase down – it was unzipped and inside I could see various yellowed pieces of paper in a state of perpetual disarray. His tweed jacket was much too big for him and his unpolished shoes were coming undone. Although he was a respected academic at the university, he played drums for a Caribbean steel band in his spare time, and on this evening he whisked me into his arms and started trying out a new drumbeat on my back, rhythmically chanting: "I don't drink coffee, I only drink tea."

My dad was a stirrer and continued illustrating his drumbeat – with me as his makeshift drum set – till I shrieked with laughter. He quickly said: "Jolie, hang in there, don't move, I think I've just started to get the hang of it." I froze on the spot, desperately trying to control my laughter.

My dad could also play guitar and did the most convincing Elvis impersonations in the southern hemisphere. I shared his love of music and together we improvised silly tunes on the piano or played dramatic duets. We were a potent combination! I liked my father's

Reading with my dad

Frances

favourite nickname for me, "Jolie". It made me feel like a gypsy, without a care in the world. Occasionally, though, he called me "Smorgasbord". It was way too eccentric for me. Whenever he called me that I would say, indignantly: "It's much too dramatic and it doesn't suit me. No thank you!"

I was six when my sister, Frances, was born. On the day of her birth, the air was bustling with energy. The pink blooms of the doll's powder-puff had a gossamer feel about them. When I turned my head, I could see the cobalt blue wing of a malachite kingfisher making its descent over the dam on the hill. We went to visit my mom in the Settlers Hospital; my first time in a hospital. When we got to her room, my mom gave me a bewildered look: "Gita, why do you have those puffed cheeks?"

Through clenched teeth, I managed to utter a few barely audible words: "I don't breathe in hospitals. I'm scared of catching germs . . .!"

A few days after our visit, my personal porcelain doll, Frances, had arrived home. Miriam Kolosa and I launched into bathing, powdering and holding her tightly.

Miriam had been part of our family for aeons. One Sunday, just before my eighth birthday, I went outside: The early morning air was filled with the rasping sound of cicadas and grasshoppers. Miriam called to me from the far side of the house and her syncopated voice bounced off the maze of walls which formed part of our house: "Sisi, come here to the loquat tree to clean the copper."

Cleaning the copper pots was not really the primary objective of this excursion to the loquat tree. The real motive was to exchange giggles and a few profound thoughts. The loquats that the tree carried were devilishly sour, and every year a lot of them ended up fermenting prematurely. At the time I was convinced that the secrets that passed between Miriam and me, as well as our (sometimes gory) stories, were absorbed by them in some inexplicable way and abruptly spoiled them. The loquat tree was where our community – consisting of myself, Miriam and a whole array of garden creatures – would seek counsel and connect. Miriam was innately a social being, but had, over the years, learnt to keep to herself. The suburbs of the white people, where she had worked all her life, never had much of a village life.

The loquat tree was neatly planted right there in the middle of the back garden beside the washing line, and the garden was spread out before me like an island, with poinsettias and petunias which my mom continued to plant, claiming that she was entitled to some succour in the dry climate of the Eastern Cape. Miriam had told me that the loquat tree had, even before my birth, always been the point around which everything and everyone associated with our house orbited.

I scuttled across the lawn and Miriam proclaimed loudly (for the umpteenth time): "Lovey, you are much too thin. One of these days, you will disappear into thin air. More mealie porridge for you to fill out those stick limbs of yours!"

I wasn't that exceptionally scrawny. The thing was that Miriam had ample flesh on her bones and anyone who dared not resemble her was the odd one out. I gave her an obstinate look and grabbed her podgy hand which pulled me down next to her.

It was turning into a late-summer scorcher that Sunday morning and I knew to soak up the light and peace and quiet before the pre-week blues would get hold of me later in the afternoon.

I said chirpily: "Miriam, give me the white stuff and I'll rub it in."

It was always nice to cloud the pots with the milky substance only to reveal the warm glow later on. Miriam was also shiny from tip to toe – her face was always glistening from the Pond's cold cream that she smoothed into her skin every morning after washing herself thoroughly with emerald green Sunlight soap.

From as far back as I could remember, Sunlight soap was my pet hate. Firstly, I detested the smell and secondly, when I was a toddler, Miriam religiously and vigorously washed me with it every morning after my spoonful of cod-liver oil, something else that wasn't particularly popular in my world of Barbie dolls and Lego. Of course, since I was a baby, the loquat tree had also played a role in this daily washing extravaganza – providing shade during mid-summer mornings while I was being washed against my will in the stainless steel tub.

We spread ourselves out beneath the blue sky, soaking in the hazy heat. I had brought along my mother's pewter jewellery box. The jewellery box was a box of wisdom, containing both my grandmothers' and my mother's dearest writings. Hopefully, one day, I would be able to add to it.

After cleaning the copper pots, Miriam would disappear to her cottage at the side of our house. It was a niche where she could put up pictures of the Queen and princess Margaret and her personal cult figure, Bessie Smith, the blues queen of the American South. With the years, the pictures faded, but she merely replaced them with the latest magazine shots. There was never even a vague sign of stagnation in Miriam's room. Every time I went in the place was spick 'n span with not even a speck of dust to be seen, an old transistor radio in the corner blurting out the news in Xhosa. She also had a vase in the corner, on the dark wooden chest, which she religiously filled with fresh flowers every second day.

The sun passed its zenith and the afternoon melted into a brooding limbo. A heavy silence settled on the garden and even the cicadas momentarily ceased their screeching. We hadn't managed to get very far with the copper pots, we had been pondering over the past week, busy with our own thoughts. For a moment, our attention was diverted by a sugarbird that fluttered in the still air. Flickers of light reflected off its shiny wings. I moved my hand towards the jewellery box. These moments were reserved for very special occasions and I felt an urgent need to read something in the magic container, since Miriam and I had chatted half the day away. We loved this dawdling on a Sunday. I took a little crinkled piece of paper from the box. It was like drawing a prize at a fête. "Eeny, meeny, miny mo." Miriam's curiosity got the better of her and she stretched over to see. I was unfolding a poem addressed to me, written by my mother:

My belly is round.
All beauty is bound up inside me.
I walk on a powder veil,
on the surface of the moon.
Little one,
are you there?
Can you feel the earth's pull?
Or do you float unawares
with the man on the moon?

Broken-winged doves

All through my childhood, I was fascinated by birds. There was something captivating about those bright creatures, suspended in air, effortlessly soaring on the wind. My mom used to read me a book about a little bird that was orphaned when it fell from its nest. It came into contact with the horrible world out there, mistaking a bulldozer for its mother and unsuccessfully seeking warmth from the machine. The book had a light blue cover with sticky marks on it – testimony to being fingered often by toddlers. The book had quite an effect on Malcolm and me. We would rescue doves with broken wings all along Wiltshire Crescent, the street in which we lived. Our rescuing equipment consisted of stainless steel pots. We would put the feathered victims inside the pots, cover them with the lids, carry them home and put them in cardboard boxes lined with leaves and grass. They rarely survived, being pestered by prying cats and dogs, or plagued by colonies of ants, which swamped their man-made nests.

We would often tear ourselves from the allure of nature when the shelves upon shelves of books beckoned us inside. Our love of stories culminated in the publication of one of my mom's children's books. She dedicated the book to her children. We swelled with pride and joy. In our eyes, our mom was a literary genius. She told us stories of flying children and aliens, as well as scary ghost stories that had been passed down through the generations from my great-grandmother to my mother. They never failed to enchant us. Magical trains, animated hippopotami and nosy, big-bottomed characters unlocked undiscovered worlds for us.

More stories entered our lives through the enticing little black box in the corner of our living room. Ours wasn't the most sophisticated I'd ever seen: Despite the bunny ears, perched on top, the picture was still mostly blurred. However, we were never encouraged to watch TV. I once overheard my mom saying laughingly to a friend: "I think they much prefer a glass of Nestlé chocolate milk and a nice book before bed!"

Nonetheless, I was obsessed with our first TV set. I would be glued to it every Tuesday at four o'clock in the afternoon when my favourite children's show would come up. It was about a baby bird with a broken wing and there was a theme song that was sung soulfully in minor chords: "If Only Cheep Could Fly". I would often chant it almost ritualistically. I still remember many evenings sitting in front of the hazy screen, relishing a packet of Rowntree's Fruit Gums and listening to the enchanting theme song of *The Thorn Birds* and the riveting introductory line: "a love – unattainable, forbidden, forever . . ."

Perhaps because of the stringent rules concerning TV watching, a prominent feature of my childhood was the cinema, His Majesty's. The town gathered in this movie house of Fifties charm. I was convinced that the Grahamstown grapevine had its roots here. The velvet curtains, dramatically draped on either side of the rows of seats, had a sort of weathered wisdom about them, as if they had absorbed the town's melodrama and gossip. The plastic chairs failed miserably at being comfortable and throughout a movie it felt as if your sitting bones were digging through the bucket seat.

One day I went to see *ET* with Malcolm and some friends. When we all walked out into the glaring sunlight after the movie, everyone looked down in an attempt to hide their tear-stained cheeks. But I heard my friends exclaiming loudly and pointing at the back of my head: "What's that in your hair, Margs!?" My hand reached up into my hair and I felt a gooey blob of chewing gum firmly rooted in my recently cut bob hairstyle. I felt a pang of intense pity for poor ET as I stood in the middle of a mob of children, pointing their fingers at me and laughing loudly. Instantly I knew ET's feeling of otherness.

There was one other instance in which I felt this otherness: I started to get asthma and the doctor told me to swim it away. My mom promptly responded by enrolling me (and Malcolm) for swimming lessons that took place at the crack of dawn. We were left to a merciless instructor who hurled abuse at us when our heads were above water: "You miserable little drowning rats! Get your act together!" He screamed instructions at us when our heads were below: "Keep your fingers together when you do the stroke and don't – and I repeat – don't come up for breath only on one side!" It was a recipe for disaster that left both of us capable of mustering only a rudimentary doggy paddle.

I much preferred playing with my canary yellow hula-hoop. I could keep the hula-hoop going for four minutes flat while kneeling, clapping my hands and turning around.

Another activity that I loved was unwrapping the Chappies that I bought at Naran's corner café, and blowing exaggerated bubbles of bright pink gum. Sometimes I would bunk Sunday school, guiltily ignoring that source of higher guidance and swapping it for the writing on the back of the wrappers. I would sit amongst the sedge flowers between the dam and the railway line on the hill while reading those erudite *Did You Know*'s.

I remember a blistering December afternoon with the mid-day

Malcolm and I

sun beating down on us. Malcolm and I dawdled towards a yesterday-today-and-tomorrow bush at the bottom of the garden. My mom called out in a far-away tone of voice: "Peanut-butter sandwiches for you two. You need some flesh on those bones, sweeties!"

In a flurry of arms and legs, we scuttled to the kitchen and came back, trying to balance trays filled with thickly sliced sandwiches and glasses of icy orange cordial. Starving, we sat down under the shrub, where we attacked the food with a vengeance.

From the tomato box of secrets that we kept under the shrub carrying small purple and white flowers, we unearthed a book called *It's a Wonderful World*. I had hidden it there and told Malcolm: "Cross your heart and hope to die. If Ma finds out, she'll take it to the stuffy study again."

I couldn't find it in my heart to force it in between other dull books in a dark bookshelf. Malcolm giggled, but made a solemn promise.

The spine of the book was unravelling and the pages had begun to fade, developing a yellowish tinge. In bold letters it proclaimed: "A treasury of knowledge all in colour". I turned to page five, unable to contain my excitement, and shoved the book onto Malcolm's lap so he would read to me. He put on a tour guide demeanour and started reading: "The Gypsies' homes on wheels . . . Five hundred and fifty years ago there appeared in Europe wandering bands of a handsome, independent race, fond of music, dance and song: the Gypsies."

Abruptly I interrupted him: "You know, we've got Gypsy blood. Grandma has been to all four corners of the earth. And one day I'm going to marry a real Scandinavian prince . . ."

As if entranced by my words, Malcolm sprang to his feet and cried: "Well, I'm going to search for enemies on the hill." We always imagined hordes of neighbourhood children threatening our gang's fort on the hill.

He left me gazing into the turquoise sky, imagining how different my life would be as a Gypsy: I would rub noses with an Eskimo, swing wildly on the arms of a windmill and follow the great herds of reindeer with the Lapps, all in one week.

The sun started mellowing and a lonely bateleur eagle flew over me in its quick and quiet way, crying out sharply. I got to my feet and went to look for Malcolm who was still playing on the hillside. Dusk, a charcoal cloak, was rapidly enfolding us, but despite the stillness I could feel a thunderstorm approaching.

During the day time there was always a sense of control, but at that moment we were like thistledown going on an unknown journey, being tossed around by air currents. I felt deeply unsure, as if I were blindfolded, but the air was bustling with activity. Lizards were scurrying in the undergrowth and a spotted eagle owl was frenetically flying about. It settled in a Jerusalem thorn tree, coldly peering at

27

me. The rims of its eyes were red and the centres were intensely black, drawing me into its binocular-like vision. Then Malcolm tugged at me from behind and I quickly swirled around, looking into his relieved, but frightened eyes.

It started to rain and we scrambled towards the house, picking up speed and huddling closely together in a mutual attempt to seek a bit of warmth. Suddenly, a vacant look crossed Malcolm's eyes and, as if besieged by an electric current, he started dancing wildly, catapulting through the veld towards home, with arms and legs flapping in all directions. I also started dancing a shamanic earth dance and joined Malcolm in his trance-like state through the shrubs.

In the east, more dark thunderclouds gathered in a furious display. Varicose veins of lightning traced the sky and mapped out hitherto undiscovered ways and routes. It was as if this celestial spectacle was nature's way of alleviating the earth's tension. As we passed, a bull terrier dropped its tail in submission and whimpered at a back door.

At last, we'd made our way to the garden gate, the earthy smell of the compost heap intermingling with the nocturnal scent of petunias. Miriam was standing under the loquat tree, frantically stripping clothes off the washing line. She looked up at the sight of two delicate children standing forlornly under the livid skies, and in a blind maternal rush she darted towards us. Her hips swayed from side to side while she took turns at piggybacking each of us to the porch. We threw ourselves over the threshold, drenched and bedazzled. We felt a sense of pride as if we'd just successfully completed an integral rite of passage, but my parents were beside themselves with worry. My mom dried us, dressed us warmly and tucked us into bed with hot chocolate and pancakes. I felt warm and sheltered: I wished for this bliss to last forever.

Even the thunderstorm was safely out there. Through the window I could see the lightning or the impundulu as it was known around those parts. Miriam once described it: "It is a white bird with bright red marks on it. When I was a child, men in my village sometimes tried to kill it with assegais before it could get to the earth." As I thought of imaginary assegais protecting us from all extraneous elements I fell into a deep sleep.

Uprooting

At the age of twelve I had to leave my beloved Miriam, the loquat tree and the succulents and centipedes of the veld. We were "blown" towards the Cape. On the day of our departure, we were all jam-packed into my dad's fleece-white Mercedes. The mid-summer's day was scorching, and the encroaching bush on the hill seemed to want to tie us down and hold us back. The sun was crawling up in the sky like an insistent insect. I could hardly breathe in the sluggish air; trails of sweat were trickling down my breastbone. The wide expanse of the hill looked implacable. The grey leaves of lamb's ears that grew along the national road twitched as we drove past. A warm wind from the mountain tickled the orange mass of flowers on the avenue of African flame trees that curtained the road. The landscape on the hill seemed to be pierced by the bitter aloes growing by the roadside. A lone eagle aimlessly circled a specific patch of sky.

We moved to Stellenbosch where the vineyards stretched out into the horizon in shades of orange and red on the mellow days of autumn. But the beauty of the Boland made no impression on me. The blue Boland mountains looked hazy and self-righteous and my heart yearned for the modest landscape of the Eastern Cape: donkey carts in dust, ghoenafigs and the shrill cry of hadedas at dusk. The power of the Eastern Cape lies in the humble character of things. The most powerful images come in a simple form: labourers standing laughing amongst dongas in a dirt road in the township, a child playing in the mingling light of a monkey's wedding.

On my first day of school, I cycled up the road to our new house, balancing five books on the back seat of my bike. The bike started to swing violently, unsteadily, and all the books fell off. I tried to shrug it off as a result of the pent-up nervousness I had been feeling all day long at my new school. But at the back of my mind something kept bothering me. Never before had I lost control so suddenly and inexplicably. I went down on my haunches to pick up the pile of books, but I couldn't figure out how to get the books back onto the bike while holding it up. Too many unusual movements were required. I thought frantically: how am I going to coordinate this? My eyes met those of a boy who had stopped to help me. He held up the bike and I passed him the books. I had seen him earlier on in the day. He was beautiful. My heart started racing, I blushed and hoped that he hadn't noticed anything strange about me. He handed the books back to me and I quickly started to push my bike up the last stretch towards home, continuing to notice the first signs of this momentary loss of balance. It was subtle, almost imperceptible, but I imagined people were staring at me from behind curtains and doors, watching this strange girl with funny balance, teetering past them. I could see hundreds of people studying me from behind binoculars, climbing up trees to have a better view. I cringed, wishing for a way to "tiptoe through the paths of my life". If I could just walk softly on the balls of my feet, the world wouldn't notice me; I would just become part of the myriad in the street, strangers who trundled past, listlessly.

I looked at my little sister's carefree childhood and yearned for my own. Frances was six at the time. It was a Saturday afternoon and a red-eyed dove made a rasping sound as it landed in the first warm breeze of the afternoon that stole around the corner of our front porch. Everyone was having a siesta, but Frances was playing in the neatly manicured garden which was overshadowed by the mountains. As I watched, she scuttled into the house, an almost tangible sense of mischief about her. I wondered what she was up to this time. Frances had always been a busy-bee; industriously watering my mom's rose garden, baking chocolate cakes and filling up our kitchen in Stellenbosch with water so as to create a swimming pool (the last of which proved to be a less than popular decision with my parents). Every day she would grandiosely relive bits and pieces of her day's adventures. Her tales were fragmentary; a kaleidoscopic mishmash of excitement. Invariably her stories were larger than life: a technicoloured snake-worm that she had encountered at arm's length; an inexplicable UFO in the grey light of dusk. The whole family was instantly alerted and held in suspense for weeks on end.

Earlier that year, Malcolm had decided to take advantage of his little sister's impressionable nature: he had dressed up as the Easter bunny on Easter Sunday. The whole family sat on the front porch, pretending not to notice as a white figure ran across the lawn. At the last moment I exclaimed loudly and pointed at the strange apparition in the garden. Frances looked up from her book and saw a white blur disappear round the corner. From that day onward, until she was much older, Frances adamantly and wholeheartedly believed in the existence of the Easter bunny. It was an unquestionable fact and she was hellbent on sharing her revelation with everyone who stepped into our family's orbit.

Despite the success of Malcolm's practical joke, I had noticed that there was something slightly unsteady about this particular Easter bunny. Amidst the light bonhomie of family tradition, I felt a hollowness in my stomach. It was a feeling that I had felt before, on the day I had seen the girl in the wheelchair: a sense of familiarity or recognition. It was unnerving, but I smiled and kept a lid on my dismay.

We had gone to my mom's family's holiday house in Hermanus ever since I could remember. We went again for a week in September of 1990. My granny Rina was there every year, making spectacular breakfasts, complete with melon and filter coffee. While the rest of the family would stretch out their sleep as long as possible, her laughter would ring through the house from the time the first shafts of sunlight nudged her awake. Her beaming smile displayed her trademark feature, the gap between her front teeth. She would spray generous amounts of Blue Grass perfume behind my ears and wrists, calling out Coco Chanel's words: "Always remember, my child, a woman without perfume, is a woman without a future . . ."

Being with Granny Rina was like bathing in clouds of white bubble bath. She made one feel angelic. We christened the blancmange pudding that we'd always made "Grandma's cheek" in honour of her complexion.

That year, Frances and I ran hand in hand down the hill to go to the mermaid's pool that we'd come across the previous year. That was when I discovered that I could no longer move down a slope effortlessly. It felt a bit as if I was careening on ice towards the bottom of the hill. Perhaps I was just tired, I thought, as I pointed at a jumping whale in the bay in front of us.

At the age of fourteen I remember going on another holiday: a weekend get-away to a lush forest area in the Southern Cape. I was becoming a woman, but I couldn't ease into the new soft contours. Over time, the loss of balance had gradually become more pronounced. We went on a hike through the dense forest, all of us absorbed in our own thoughts. I was irritated by the labyrinth of the forest unfolding before me and the way in which my body seemed to follow its own will. Its lack of own direction intensified the confusion. I wasn't enjoying the dialogue between my body and nature with its uneven footpaths and crawling undergrowth.

During the first part of the hike, my dad must have noticed something different in the way I was walking because he looked concerned and asked me to move carefully down some steps by placing both feet on each step before attempting another. I became upset and told them that I was going back. Soon after I had turned back towards where our log cabin was, I started an uncontrolled dance, and as I moved, I found that I had to invest my undivided attention into trying to make my legs move the way I wanted them to. My head was humming so that everything else was shut out; it was as if the intense concentration smothered all sensation . . . I couldn't see or feel anything familiar, especially not an awareness of myself amongst the trees surrounding me.

Luckily, a very robust hiker with two solid legs like tree-trunks confronted me. He looked at the bewildered, derailed girl before him and frogmarched me back to the cabin, convinced that I'd been intoxicated by some exotic forest plant. Perhaps I had eaten the seeds of a pomegranate or picked the blooms of a narcissus: I could feel the betrayal of my own body by its own cells. I had learnt about Persephone whose dance with the other goddesses in the sun-soaked field of flowers was interrupted by Hades, god of the underworld. She had picked the forbidden narcissus flower and was abducted to a cold and wintry land. I felt that land in my bones . . . somehow I knew that my days of dancing in the sun were reaching an end . . . I thought of Hades abducting me from my life as I once knew it. He was putting a halt to my dance of willow leaves.

Back at the log cabin I sat outside for a while, trying to relieve my stiff and contracting muscles. The sickle of a moon was appearing in the sky and slowly I felt part of it all again, part of the earth and the sky. The rigidity of my body was melting away and I felt myself fleshing out. The crescent moon was crowning me, but I still yearned for golden winged sandals to release me from the earth's pull.

At this stage, as a teenager in full bloom, I became self-conscious and preoccupied with my body as all teens do. I wanted to blend in with the rest and hated this difference; this illness that was like an alien intruder. I continued to imagine that there was an "invisible audience" that was watching my every move. I wanted to flee to the opposite side of the earth, become a nameless Gypsy. I would get performance anxiety de luxe. This caused the lack of co-ordination and balance to get worse. When I felt self-conscious, I would try so hard to control any sign of imbalance, that the concentration and focus would make it worse. When I had to receive a prize on stage at a prize-giving ceremony, the world would accelerate and the earth under my feet would become a seesaw.

But I was convinced of the moral logic of "practice makes perfect". I had always believed in this gem of advice which had firmly taken root in me from a young age in super-organised school systems. Once again I was convinced that my rock-firm belief in this wisdom would come to the rescue. I was adamant that I could perfect my gait. Sometimes I would climb up and down the stairs in the middle of the night like a deranged person, as if I was indulging in some secretive obsession. I refused to give in to the mad force that had suddenly started to inhabit my body. I felt an overwhelming sense of accomplishment when I managed to go down the stairs without wobbling.

But even after all the practising, my first instinct was to cower in the nearest corner when I found myself in public spaces. I detested choir performances where I normally had to walk up on narrow choir benches. At moments like these I would fervently pray for competent balance while walking up and down. My validity as a human being was on the line. If I should trip or fall all my self-respect, self-worth and dignity would go down the drain. By some miracle, I never once tripped during my seven years of choir singing.

Water dance

She walks past
a jelly fish,
washed out by sea tides,
discarded foetus.

She dances the hesitant
puppet-waltz
of a sea gull struggling
in a tugging wind.

And sees
at dusk
a sea swallow
sweeping high above the sand,
wings widely spanned.

Silk stockings

Parallel to my experience at the time was my brother's. He had similar symptoms of the same condition, but was two years older than I. Since his early teens, I had noticed that his bulky school bag, which he carried around on his back, seemed to throw him slightly off balance. Why was his bag so much heavier than everyone else's? When he slung the bag over the one shoulder, he looked unsteady and had to spend a few seconds recovering before moving again. He had always been stoical and never mentioned anything to us. He seemed to give more thought to his heavy-metal music, gelled hair and *MAD* magazines. Was it possible that we were both experiencing the same odd balance disturbances? I didn't want to think about it. It could not be happening . . .

At this time, we were becoming more and more frightened. Luckily, our school environment was gentle. No-one asked us any questions, they just tried to help. People did not make a fuss and Malcolm continued to be a popular member of the cricket club.

My mom had been taking Malcolm to doctors since she had first noticed his uneven walk. When they saw that I moved in the same way, they must have realised it was the same condition and decided it wasn't necessary to subject me to the same merciless medical testing.

After all, the answer had always been: "Nothing serious is wrong . . . only a bit of clumsiness . . . nothing to worry about . . ." This brought no relief, only anxiety. My mom camouflaged her desperate sadness, knowing that this diagnosis was not the correct one.

But, as the loss of balance and co-ordination became more frequent and more obvious in both Malcolm and myself, and as my family and close friends came to know about it, my confusion and terror mounted. We carried on searching the country for doctors who could help.

During this time, Malcolm went for an examination. A nurse wanted to find out what he was allergic to and he answered: "R & B music." She laughed and asked if he had any complaints. My mom told her that Malcolm never complained, making it impossible for anyone to know what he needed. They both looked at him imploringly and he replied: "There are so many things that I could complain about. If I were to start now, I would never stop. For example, I could complain about the state of Springbok rugby for a week."

In time, for Malcolm and my parents, the long search for an answer came to an end. They found a doctor who came up with the right diagnosis. At home, everyone was subdued, but I didn't really understand, no-one told me what was going on. I merely overheard titbits of information and managed to string together that Malcolm had a rare neurological condition, Friedreich's ataxia, which made it hard to walk. I had no idea what this actually meant, but I didn't have the courage to ask more. I wasn't really part of this process – I didn't feel that I had the right to know. I would have done anything for him to be well again. However, the information that I did have was slowly sinking in and I watched, amazed, as Malcolm continued to be his smiling, teasing self. My brave brother.

Malcolm recently told me how he felt at that time: "You know," he

Malcolm

said, "I could live with the thought that I had ataxia, but I couldn't bear the idea that you also had it."

It was becoming clear that I probably suffered from the same disorder, but I needed my family to tell me this. I needed them to say something. I felt that I didn't have the right to also have the condition. It was self-indulgent, presumptuous. Here I was, burdening my family even further. If I didn't think about it, maybe it would go away. So, I suppressed it and for three years never mentioned the unmentionable.

The experience was also shaping Malcolm as a person – and it was frightening to see how he was being whittled into something else than the barefoot boy he had been in Grahamstown. Malcolm wasn't self-conscious. He would run around the rugby field like a drunk and flash a couple of disarming smiles at the girls standing on the sidelines. I would have cringed at displaying my eccentric gait in such a way. I loved Malcolm for the way in which he was handling the whole thing, yet I tried to avoid him as much as possible. I felt awkward and inadequate. Malcolm would try and draw me out of myself, yelling at the top of his voice: "Chill out, Marge!"

Although we were coping with it differently, he still held up a mirror image of myself. I wanted to hide from it. I could not tell anybody, because I did not think that anyone would understand – how could they when I didn't even understand the peculiar symptoms myself.

Those peculiar symptoms were bulldozing their way into that domain in my life that I had always thought of as my safe haven – playing the piano, which had always been bliss.

The piano and I have an intricate history. Probably from the moment my legs could carry me and my podgy fingers manage some form of fine co-ordination, I felt an insistent pull towards the rickety piano at the other side of the house. We had a strangely elongated house and the piano was conveniently placed in the room furthest from all the bedrooms. This made it possible to indulge in irritating little tunes like "Chopsticks" during ungodly hours of the morning while my parents were still blissfully asleep.

At the age of five, my nursery school class was practising for the annual Nativity play in the town hall. On this particular day the teacher who normally accompanied our Christmas carols was off sick and left us feeling lost, a sorry excuse for holy angels. This was where I stepped in and offered my inexperienced skills at the piano. I think the teachers were caught off guard and were so utterly baffled by this five-year-old's suggestion that they speechlessly nodded their heads. I don't think there was anything sublime about my version of "Silent Night" or remotely upbeat about "We Wish You a Merry Christmas", but my friends cheerfully sang to my slightly off-key playing and there must have been something amusing about a little child attempting such a grown-up thing.

I grabbed the first opportunity to take piano lessons in my first year of school. I had composed a song that I was very proud of and subsequently played to my teacher. She seemed chuffed with it and promptly made a rough notation of the tune. The next day she presented me with a very professional-looking piece of music which she entitled, "Minuet in C". I positively beamed, feeling like the incarnation of one of the big composers for the rest of the day. She firmly consolidated in me a love for music, so that I continued with music lessons and took it as a subject in high school, despite having to endure tortuous eisteddfods judged by solemn-looking adults.

But then, at the age of sixteen, my love for the piano started to turn sour. My left arm muscles began to weaken, slowly making it impossible for me to make the music I loved. Only a year before, I had been labelled a promising musician and I found it impossible to tell my tutor that my progressively poor technical skills had nothing to do with lack of practice. I launched into a frenzy of scale practising, locking myself into the music room during breaks and tying my arm to the doorknob with a pair of tights to keep it from giving in.

My mother

I realised after a while that my arm's strange behaviour was only the tip of the iceberg and that I was failing dismally at my frantic attempts to cling onto my love of playing the piano.

I only recently found out that at the school's annual music concert of that year my mom sat next to my teacher. She gently asked my mom: "Is something the matter with Marguerite?" My mom, who had hoped that no-one else could notice the imbalance, went an ashen colour. She wasn't ready to talk about it and could only look at my teacher in dismay.

It was about that time that I realised I would have to make some hard decisions and exchange music for another subject. One afternoon I told my mom about my arm. I wanted to stay calm, but my voice quivered: "I have to stop my music . . ." She looked stricken and took me in her arms. I stammered: "If I have Malcolm's illness, I don't want to live . . ."

There were no words.

Any other school subject would have been a poor substitute, not a patch on music, a passion that had enveloped me since I could barely walk. The subject that fitted into that time slot was science, which was almost the antithesis of music and, to crown it, up two flights of stairs.

At the age of seventeen I went on an overseas holiday. It was probably the worst time to do this. Yet, I went on a camping trip in a bus through Turkey with my cousin and a group of young people. I continued to experience signs of imbalance and lack of co-ordination. Needless to say, I felt greatly uncomfortable in my own skin. No-one asked me about it and for the most part they pretended not to notice it, so that I began to hope that it was all just a figment of my imagination. During the whole trip I tried to bottle up the confusion that I felt and to tuck it away in the furthest reaches of my mind.

But then, one night in Istanbul, as I was getting into the bus to fetch my sleeping bag, the bus driver, a gruff Australian with a heavy accent, confronted me and said huskily: "Why are you always drunk? You should be ashamed of yourself, lassie!"

He knew exactly how to hurt me most. I don't know what the man thought. Perhaps that I had been a foetal alcohol syndrome baby who grew up to become an inebriated teenager, drunk every second of the day?

A jolt ran through my body and I struggled to pull myself together. I groped for something to say and managed to croak some meaningless guttural sound, which probably strengthened his suspicions. I got out of the bus, assaulted by feelings of self-loathing and, inexplicably, of guilt.

Back in South Africa, my difference and unease were intensified and I became shy and withdrawn. More than ever before, I kept to the fringes of groups and shied away from the limelight. I felt like an extraterrestrial with an invisible audience. After having felt anger in recent years about my parents' lack of openness, I have now come to understand that they wanted to shelter me from the harsh world of hospitals and examinations. But the lack of information about the disorder was killing me at the time. There had to be *more* to the scraps of knowledge that I had. I had to claim the right to a diagnosis for myself.

My voice was shaking when I scheduled an appointment with the neurologist who had diagnosed Malcolm. My mom understood and supported my decision. She was with me when he told me, in a flat, metallic tone of voice: "Marguerite, you suffer from a rare neurological disorder, Friedreich's ataxia. It is an inherited, progressive disorder of the nervous system. A genetic mutation affects the production of a certain protein, frataxin, within the cells. A lack of this protein means that iron levels cannot be maintained and that iron then builds up in the cells, causing structural damage. It is a degenerative condition and a person who has it has an average life expectancy of thirty-five."

Oh God, there *was* so much more to it . . . In other words, I was being poisoned by iron . . . I couldn't say anything . . . An angel of death had given me a message, stark and grim in its finality.

My head droned with shock. I wanted to beg for this not to be true, but I whispered politely: "Thank you . . ."

He also looked stricken.

A thin and yellowed pamphlet was given to me. I opened it, dumbfounded. Inside all the facts of the disorder, *our* disorder, were neatly lined up in a succession of bullet points. Was this possible? My whole life was diminished to these few printed words. How could everything boil down to this flimsy piece of paper in my hand? I started to read it, incredulously: "The disorder is slowly progressive, usually resulting in an inability to walk within eight to ten years following onset of symptoms. During the course of the disorder, leg muscles continue to weaken, but with the aid of a wheelchair, affected individuals may maintain independence . . ." The piece of paper fell to the ground and my mind stopped working.

I was alone – immensely alone. The tables were going to turn on me even more as the condition progressed, leaving me out in the cold. I was timid and overwhelmed. My mom put her arm protectively around me and we sat there in silence.

Everything blurred in front of my eyes. All sounds made a jarring noise, beating insistently at my eardrums. The doctor's mouth was moving robotically, as if he were mute, and the fluorescent light above him seemed to sear my skin. I tried to react politely during the rest of the visit, but all I could think of was that a life like an arid plain stretched out in front of me. The place was smothering me. The pot plants on his windowsill were limp, dry at the fringes. I couldn't breathe.

Trying to come to terms with my new reality

The words

Five minutes of silence
for you
who have been stricken
by words

The walking one
who is not really alive
the one who has left
without resurrection
or ceremony

But I pray for you
for an arising
of the flesh
that was sucked dry
by the words

I pray that you will find
your own voice
that will initially whisper

and then – sing

In order to confirm our diagnosis, we were advised to see a neurologist at the Princess Alice Hospital. On my way there, I kept thinking how glamorous and inviting the place sounded. I conjured up images from *Alice in Wonderland* and thought of royal tea parties. What a deceptive name for a dreary hospital! The only connection was the labyrinth of shiny grey corridors, sharply reflecting sunlight, somehow reminding me of a looking glass. But this didn't comfort me. As we walked down never-ending corridors, I felt deeply self-conscious. The place was projecting a thousand images of me, magnifying my imbalance, amplifying my footfalls.

In the doctor's office, we had to undergo a series of rigorous tests, exposing what to me felt like my most painful "secret". I was instructed to walk in a straight line, one foot precisely in front of the other. Then I had to stand dead still on one spot, close my eyes and keep my balance. Next, I had to touch the tip of my left forefinger and my nose with the tip of my right forefinger. Needless to say, I dismally failed at all of them. I kept on castigating myself for not being able to keep my composure under pressure, but with the piercing eyes of my brother, mother and the doctor analyzing my every move, I was doomed to fail. I was humiliated; an inebriated nobody who was, in fact, sober and under eighteen. I was defying the natural order. I was a failure as a human being, bound to be disqualified from the human race. Malcolm didn't do much better. We were the court jesters of this "royal" hospital.

In spite of the confirmation of this diagnosis my mom was determined to create a semblance of normality in our family. She continued the Herculean task of ensuring that her children were involved in life, to the best of their ability. She would point out the beauty of the sun's broken crystal-shards on the surface of the fishpond; together, we chuckled at the startlingly coloured caterpillar tenaciously clinging to the stem of a crimson glory in the rose garden. In this way she gently coaxed us into forgetting that we were always teetering on the edge of a cliff. In between there were the endless trips to physiotherapists, naturopaths, biokineticists, etc. And she wrote reams of poetry for us about brave, bespectacled teenagers.

Malcolm never experienced the process of diagnosis as a watershed. For him, it didn't signify any change. For a long time he had known that something serious was wrong with his body. He and my dad continued to play cricket, even though his loss of balance made it virtually impossible. They merely figured out ways to work around it.

I know now that my parents suffered unexpressed pain and confusion in those years. Sometimes, on summer nights, my dad would start plucking his guitar strings and wistfully croon a tune from *Sergeant Pepper's Lonely Hearts Club Band*. I couldn't seem to reach him any more. He seemed to find solace in his work as a professor of economics at the university.

For all of us, the diagnosis put a label to what we were experiencing. And for the first time we more or less knew (or thought we knew) what the future held. Our coping mechanism was to grin and bear the shadows, not to make any fuss. We almost made ourselves believe that nothing out of the ordinary was going on. I have come to understand that it was my parents' way of protecting us, of raising us as "normally" as possible.

As our balance became more and more shaky, the physical environment was adjusted. We had to learn new ways of singing with the cicadas and flying up high with the swallows. We had to let go of our old selves, but didn't know how. The memories of the Jerusalem thorn tree, the hadedas and the sugar biscuits were blurred, mere vestiges of memory. Malcolm and I had become the doves that we used to rescue all along Wiltshire Crescent. We had to leave the roles that we had always known, we had to become those frightened creatures of the twilight, in transit to an unknown place.

Permanently drunk

I went to Stellenbosch University in 1997 to start my tertiary education. Friendship, confidences, gossip and laughter are what women's residences are made of. I envied the girls who carried cups of tea and coffee up and down the stairs to one another's rooms. I, the stranger, unknown to myself and to others, stayed in my room. A flight of stairs, that I had to negotiate a few times every day, had quickly become my enemy.

Here, in the heartland of healthy, robust youth, I realised for the first time how soft and accepting my school's environment had been. My friends and I could laugh easily, lie around for ages listening to The Cranberries or humming songs from The Cure. They didn't expect me to talk about what was happening to me. But in this strange place I looked permanently drunk, my legs going forward of their own accord as my balance and coordination gradually became worse. I sorely needed to cling to the hand railings, but something in me refused to give in to this mad force in my body, slowly claiming every cell for itself. Holding onto the railing, I told myself, would mean admitting defeat, surrendering to what I thought of as weakness.

Symptoms of ataxia had by now started to manifest themselves even more prominently and I had reduced my life to a battle strategy.

My roommate, Justine, had a shaved head and nose ring. She

didn't look like someone who could easily be shocked. So one night, in our first week, over two cups of green tea and the I Ching, I told her. She was the first friend in whom I ever confided and she said: "No ways . . . just shout if you need some help, will you?" But I didn't know how to ask anyone for help and we never talked about it again. While Justine carried on with her busy life as an art student, I started to straightjacket my experiences by isolating myself in my room in the residence. My life was a trek on a dark and uneven footpath through an underworld; I felt marked by my difference. I didn't have any network of support anymore: No-one here had any inkling of the nature of my condition or conception of the fact that, over the course of a few years, I had slowly been losing my ability to walk. I couldn't begin to explain it to the girls around me who were agonizing about the length of the dresses they would wear to the next dance. I had to summon all my courage to go to lectures, let alone go to dances.

I measured my value as a person in terms of the flights of stairs that I could successfully climb. The staircases in the residence were targeted as prime practising sites. Sometimes, when all the voices had died down, around midnight, I would slip out of bed and head for the staircase near my room. Only when I could successfully conquer the flight of stairs – ascend or descend it without holding on to the hand railing – would I allow myself to crawl back into bed. It was the only place of comfort that I knew, the only place where I could be myself. In my first week there, just as the initiation was being wrapped up and girls' excited voices were bouncing off the corridor walls, I fell down a flight of stairs and found myself lying in a pool of blood with a broken nose. Blood was discolouring the grey tiles as Justine rushed out of our room to help me. After a while, someone came to mop up the blood and the smell of ammonia was overbearing. That lifeless mop standing in the weathered steel bucket remains imprinted in my mind. I often dreamt at night that moving staircases were eluding me, or giving way under my feet. Some nights I lay in my bed, my body racked with grief at the unbearable thought that the tide would never turn.

Shortly after the fall, as I was wending my way to class, a student shouted at me in an accusing way across the street: "Hey you, why are you always drunk?" It felt as if all conversation around me died down, as if the shrill cry of the cicadas had abruptly stopped, it was as if he had stabbed me. I just smiled apologetically, wanting to disappear into a black hole.

That question reverberated in my mind for a long time afterwards and shortly after this incident, when the ligaments in my knees started to weaken so that my legs would lock, causing me a lot of pain, I began to wonder whether there was a relationship between my pain and his shouting.

The teacup

As I carry the cup
meticulously
across the room,
I realise
in a passing moment
that it encompasses
all that ever mattered to me:
my success or failure in this life
is on the line.
It is all-consuming,
titanic,

grotesque.
All else is disproportionate
in the shadow of
its monumental dimensions.

I have to distinguish myself
as the god who has to contain
the sea of Ceylon tea in a cup,
the crucible nestled in a saucer.
Despite painstaking concentration,
tidal breakers crash over the
fine porcelain edges.

With my next cup of tea,
the journey continues:
again I try to reinstate
my former powers
of long ago.

During these harsh times, my grandmother's house in Stellenbosch
was a place of relative safety. Her house was pink like icing sugar and
stood behind a curtain of roses. In the street, little girls took turns at
skipping. Every now and then I would go to visit my grandmother,
be treated to her milk tart or the home-made vegetable soup that she
would make in winter, and listen to stories of her life as a singer in
the grand concert halls of Europe, and of how she posed to have her
legs photographed for Cameo stockings.

Grandma Greta used to visit us regularly in Grahamstown. One
day, when I was about seven years old, I was coming up the hill, back
from swimming in the dam, still shaking the last drops of water off

my shivering body. A shiny Mercedes-Benz was parked in the drive-way. A tall dame with an accomplished air about her was calling out instructions to a little bent man: her timid chauffeur. After every pause a new suitcase of a different shape and size emerged out of the car so that a train of vanity cases, hat-boxes and suitcases snaked their way up to the house. She looked in alarm at her family standing in the dust in front of her. Their clothes had been bought at church bazaars! Malcolm and I were barefoot. She smoothed out her beauti-fully fitted suit and generously tipped the chauffeur. Like the Queen of England she started striding towards the house, wafts of Joy per-fume enveloping us as we followed behind.

From the moment she entered, she seemed omnipotent in the house. She eyed Malcolm and me with interest and cried: "I have great aspirations for you two savages. When I was small I had to have my hair shingled! You two have been lucky so far, getting to run around like hairy rascals: half-naked . . . Running loose on the hill is one thing, but does it do anything to expose those hidden talents, asleep beneath the surface?"

I quickly said: "Well, we do watch the *Muppet Show* and get bub-ble-gum stuck in our hair at His Majesty's. Last year we also went to *Fiddler on the Roof . . .*"

My grandma said sweetly: "Yes, yes honey, I hear you. But what I really mean is: what do you do about your own talents? I can see Malcolm being a little Yehudi Menuhin, charming audiences world-wide with his fiddle. And as for you, young lady, be a sport and sing 'Over the Rainbow' to your travel-weary gran?"

I got up hesitantly and sang a barely recognisable version of the song. I stammered, croaked and gurgled my way through the ordeal. Grandma Greta first looked pale with shock and then started clap-ping her hands gingerly. We all began to chuckle and our amused laughter rang through the house. By the time we finished, the glamorous diva pretended to look quite alarmed: "Well, I must be honest . . . That did nothing to soothe your gran's sore bones. To bed with you, then." She shooed us away with a flick of her hand, promising to come and read to us later.

By the time my mom came to say good night to us, a picture of perfect peace and tranquillity greeted her. Grandma Greta had snuggled in between us and started to read a bedtime story. The story was called "Outside Over There" and was very off-beat, about goblins and kidnapping. Grandma explained: "The three of us ditched Cinderella for this story of mystery and suspense. I remember my childhood infested with wholesome little books full of moral lessons."

My mom laughed: "Yes, I'm sure you scoffed at anything that was 'the done thing.'"

Grandma looked impressed by her daughter-in-law's insight: "Parochial is the word, honey. I never take to anything that reeks of convention. When roller skates became all the rage, I was the only girl in the neighbourhood who owned a pair. It wasn't considered quite appropriate for young girls . . . when I was a bit older I smoked Golden Flake cigarettes while showing off my legs in Red Seal Silk Hosiery – also not quite couth, you know."

My mom smiled: "I can't imagine you having worn tight corsets as a young girl."

"While other girls of my age wore petticoats, I insisted on the shortest frocks available in the fashion industry," Grandma replied.

Malcolm and I started yawning. Gran said quickly: "I apologise . . . I'm sure the two of you are not in the least interested in your archaic gran's childhood tales. Actually, I'm not that much of a dinosaur, though. *Peter Pan* was one of my favourite books as a child, and didn't you two ask for that as tomorrow night's story?"

55

Our eyes started twinkling instantly. Gran gave us a cunning look and said: "May Tinkerbell bewitch you in your dreams tonight, my darlings!"

In the intervening years she began to carry her significant corpulence with flair and had the legendary ability to dish up a story as if it were a sumptuous meal. Her face was always bright and animated, accentuated with a sturdy layer of make-up. She was the perfect cross between a provocative Mae West, a sultry Greta Garbo and an evocative Marlene Dietrich. My visits to her while I was doing my first year at Stellenbosch, seemed to soothe me and momentarily release me from the choking grip that the illness had on me. On all my visits, without exception, she would be dressed to a 't'. She would smoothe out a beautifully tailored suit before collapsing on the chaise longue and crooning in a husky voice: "One vhisky on the rocks and don't be stingy, baby!"

I couldn't imagine her cloistered in a little retirement village with a yellow canary in a cage as her only companion, or fondly staring at family photos from a time long gone. Instead, I could picture her at her ripe old age skinny-dipping in the full moon. She played the inimitable role of our family's drama queen and soothsayer.

I remember on one occasion paging through one of her many art books and coming across a print of Picasso's *Guernica*. How could Hitler have classified this wondrous piece of work as "Degenerate Art"? In the right-hand corner of the print was a man stretching out his arms and fingers towards the sky. I recognised the desire in myself to reach out to the heavens and shout out my fear of loneliness and of slowly becoming paralysed.

Bath without water

She sits in the bath
and cries
till she ages,
hands and feet;
she feels her body
like a jigsaw puzzle
not working.
She sits hunched over,
white (like a dice without dots).
She knows
she's being dissolved
in water.

She hears the geyser
that groans, wants to burst.
She pulls out the plug
and sits alone in the bath
without water,
like a child hiding,
not wanting to be found.

Naked – like before the fall –
and she is cold.

One early Sunday in autumn, while still trudging through my first
year at university, I decided to go to the river that flowed through the
town. The day was warm and mellow and church bells were calling

57

to one another across town. As I sat on the wooden bench, looking at the rust-coloured leaves gently falling on the river bank, I felt synchronised with everything around me and knew that, even though my body was slowly unravelling, something larger was being woven. I remembered one of my favourite childhood stories, *Heidi*, and thought of myself living in the Swiss Alps, tending to my goats and running wildly on the mountain slopes. I longed for the freedom of my own childhood and wished that things could be different.

Irreparably injured

On the 25th of May 1998, during my second year, I was walking across the street with a friend, when I was hit by a car. I felt a stabbing pain in my left leg and the last thing that I remember was the brand name of the wheel that passed above my head – FIRESTONE.

I lost consciousness and woke up to find a whole group of people around me, sheltering me from the passing traffic. But I scarcely noticed the chaos and panic around me, because I was in a dreamlike state. Everything around me was sublime and surreal. I was tranquil and peaceful. For lack of a better description for this feeling, I will say that it felt as if angels were sending a clear and distinct message to me that I would be okay. If I were to have been reminded of these feelings two days later in hospital, I would have laughed in disbelief, for I was in severe pain for the next year – in a wheelchair for three months and on crutches for a year after that. But at the scene of the accident I felt somehow distanced from my body and maybe understood for a second or two that we are much more than physical bodies that experience the outside world with five senses.

Before I quite knew that my leg had been broken by a flash of steel, I'd lost consciousness for a while and instantly felt myself immersed in the warm, soapy water of oblivion. I was rudely awoken by a paramedic. He was speaking to his buddy and said: "She looks like a rag doll, but I think she'll make it."

After these words, I felt shocked and could feel my heart beating faster. I probably could have been more lively in an attempt to remind them that I was still conscious, but the body's natural morphine was doing its work beautifully. I was floating in a stream of slow-moving tranquillity and envisioning ethereal entities. There were two very prominent ones: the one was sylphlike and solemn, wearing a cobalt blue dress. She was responsible for the quiet bliss that was surrounding me. Then there was a plump, giggling one. She had light brown, curly hair and cute little dimples. She was giggling compulsively as if witnessing the funniest thing in her life. Needless to say, I did not share her amusement. Was she there to make me feel a little bit lighter? I had no chance to ponder whether I was having the first glimpse of my guardian angels (or some such thing), because the next moment I felt myself being wheeled into the emergency room of the hospital at an alarming speed.

It all happened in true hospital-drama style. My mobile bed was pushed into the double swinging doors that co-operatively swung a full ninety degrees away from us and then one hundred and eighty degrees backwards – all in record time. The collision startled me and I thought indignantly: What if they damaged my leg even more? Their negligence infuriated me and I half rose out of my horizontal position to speak my mind.

The sharpness of the white fluorescent lights and the medical staff's sudden movements made me feel raw, hollow and puny. I was obviously much too disruptive, because the next moment someone plonked a mask of sorts over my mouth to silence me and keep me firmly rooted. People's voices and faces started merging together pleasantly; a cup of creamy coffee being stirred round and round.

I woke up considerably later, but I had no idea how long I'd been wandering in a subterranean world while they were fixing my leg. It was as if a long period of time had been completely erased in my consciousness and I stared around me in bewildered panic.

Demobilised

In this maximum security prison
of tamed instincts
my once malleable body
has been jolted
into this chair on wheels;
my impulses are dulled.
I quell the pangs of envy
of the mobility
I see around me:
the lifting of a finger
the animation of a face,
feelings painted on a canvas.

I'm swallowed by the ritual
of my days
devoured by my thoughts
of stark lines
and wait patiently
for the gravity of sleep
to carry me away
to that place of soft contours.

The room was submerged in twilight, although I couldn't understand where the dusk, or dawn, was coming from. I couldn't see any windows in the room and a strange green light illuminated the other three beds that I could see. The beds were surrounded by curtains and shut off from prying eyes. I could hear someone moaning from behind the curtain in the bed next to mine – it felt wrong to be sharing in this person's misery, sharing in her most intimately painful experience.

I focused on myself and could see a huge white lump at the bottom of the bed where my left leg was propped up with cushions. It felt as if I were marooned on an enormous white marshmallow, unable to move my left leg. There was some movement in my other leg, but the question was: how was I ever again going to be able to move with no balance or co-ordination, a shattered leg and a semi-functional right leg of which half of the muscles had already worn away? I certainly didn't feel inspired to attempt my first steps in this clinical cubicle with its cold, grey linoleum tiles and its pungent smell of sterilising agents.

But, while I was pondering my alien surroundings, I was startled by the sharpness of a needle, inserted in my arm. A warm and stinging liquid was travelling through my veins, easing the sharp, stabbing pains that were starting in my left leg. I was drifting into a delicious delirium. The pain that I was feeling was expelled to the corner of the room so that my body was totally free from it. The marshmallow that I was lying on was throwing me up into the air like a trampoline. The scene had suddenly transformed into a children's party.

The hospital seemed to eclipse everything else. It was so immutably there; not open to negotiation. I couldn't really remember that I even had much of a life before entering hospital.

One of the nurses looked absently at a patient next to me. The nurse's look was distant and glazed over, not seeing. I felt panicky, gave her a super-friendly smile and fervently hoped that she'd be careful with the drips and machines attached to me. Maybe she was working overtime. She looked tired and glanced at the card above my bed with my information on it. I thought anxiously: my life has suddenly shrunk, I have been reduced to a white card with information on. I don't think she would have noticed if the whole ward of patients suddenly jumped up and started doing the cancan, with drips rattling in their holders.

I was cloistered between the white walls of the hospital. Light relief came in the shape of friends and family. Justine brought me a delectable box of chocolates and we talked about university – it all seemed so distant. Louise and Carine, my best friends from school, brought me more chocolates. They were Belgian and expensive! Murphy's law – just when I couldn't face sweet things! There was a girl in the bed next to me. She looked weak, as if she'd been there for a long time and would still be there for a while. No-one came to visit her, except for an auntie, or friend, who dropped in one Sunday for ten minutes. I gave her my chocolates and we got into the habit of watching the soap operas together, the highlight of each day, gossiping about every tiny scandal and minute detail: "Did you see those kitsch stilettos she wore?" By the time I left, we felt joined at the hip and exchanged phone numbers.

How could I forget the first day I attempted walking to the window of the hospital room with my crutches?

I had been lying horizontally for over a month and when I got myself standing up in between my crutches, blood surged from my head down to my lower limbs. The sudden difference in circulation left my head feeling intensely sore for a few seconds. I gasped for breath and waited for the first possible moment to try an initial tentative step. One of the sisters was patiently walking beside me with the wheelchair, so that I felt safer. I was focusing so intensely on trying to keep upright that I didn't have a moment to turn to her and smile appreciatively. My legs were fluid, like seaweed . . . oh, seaweed: I longed, at that moment, to walk with my bare feet on the wet sand of the beach in Hermanus. I wanted it so much . . .

I tried to focus. The nurse was glancing up at me obliquely, looking kind and not expecting me to perform any kind of miracle of mobility. She probably thought of me as a patient, disabled. But I was a young girl, a student who had been planning to go to a dance with friends. I felt desperate, I kept thinking that mentally I did not know how to be wheelchair-bound but physically that was what I was going to be forced to become if I could not walk. I still thought of myself as climbing the branches of the loquat tree.

After ten minutes I fell backwards into the chair. The nurse went down on her haunches and took my hand. Normally, she looked highly efficient and was always on the go, but at that moment as she sat quietly, I could see thin blue veins under her skin. Her clear blue eyes were concerned and gentle. I knew at that moment that if I was to walk again, I had to be determined and forget that I ever had any knowledge of mindlessly and effortlessly being carried on my two legs.

Making that single, first step was easier said than done. Because I was in such pain and was suffering from post-traumatic depression, it felt as if I were disappearing into quicksand. Every time I tried to walk with crutches, I lost my balance and my leg pained as if knives were being stabbed into it.

I sorely needed to go home where I could breathe more easily. The goings-on in the hospital had no relation to my life.

After a month, my dad brought me back home from my stay in

hospital. That evening, my mom was standing at the kitchen counter, chopping up some vegetables. Her silky robes lightly swayed from side to side as she cut up the carrots. She wasn't wearing an apron. Although it wasn't always possible for her, she often tried to resist any constraints. Frances came into the lounge, doing her silly-walk routine, imitating a bloke from Downunder: "Hey mate, great to see yer again!" Then she quickly changed identities and did a wild Irish jig. It was good to laugh again.

As I rolled into the kitchen, my mom proudly announced: "Tonight we'll have a special meal for a special guest. Mademoiselle, everything will be done to your utmost liking. I've already adapted our regular start-of-the-week meal to nothing less than *haute cuisine*. And now I'll introduce to you our hors d'oeuvre – vegetable fajitas – made with crushed garlic, chili powder, guacamole and lots and lots of coriander. This will be followed by mushroom and okra curry, a subtle and aromatic delight, made with ginger, chillies, coriander, cumin, cardamom seeds and enough garlic to feed an army. Accompanying the curry, we'll have Provençal stuffed peppers made with true French panache. And last, but not least, uhhmm, some sort of devilish dessert will round off an evening of exotic cuisine. So brace yourself, ma chérie."

I was taken aback by her generosity and felt slightly intimidated by the rows and rows of ingredients lined up on the counters. Every conceivable space was occupied by cashew and brazil nuts, Brussels sprouts, garlic cloves, sesame seeds, Bulgarian yoghurt, etc., etc. She had already started frying fajitas for the promised starter. Clumsily handling the spatula, she pretended to do it with expert flair. For a second, I thought she was going to flick the pancake-like thing up to the ceiling hoping that it would stick, in an attempt to ascertain its level of readiness. But instead she dissected a piece of watery dough while crying out in despair. As the preparations progressed, her enthusiasm started to wilt and was replaced by semi-hysterical shrieks every now and then, just to mark the litany of little disasters that peppered our attempts. Towards the end of it all, she grew accustomed to the idea that our meal wouldn't be *haute cuisine* as initially planned, and let bygones be bygones. But, she gasped when she looked at me: From top to toe, I was covered in a green, gooey mess of guacamole. Since the counter was too high for me, I had no choice but to peel the avocados on my lap. And to worsen the situation, I couldn't keep still. My wheels were going backwards and forwards as I tried to peel away. But I had managed to mash the slippery avos, in the end, and complete the somewhat treacherous task. Up to that moment, my mother had hardly had a second to glance up from her preoccupations, but as soon as she noticed the state I was in she fussed around me, trying to wipe off the green substance that had somehow managed to get everywhere – even between the spokes of my wheelchair.

She smiled at me sympathetically. "You poor thing, you should prosecute me for slave driving."

"Don't be silly, Ma. I can't just sit silently, waiting to be served like royalty!"

She was confused about what exactly our "devilish dessert" would be, lulling her angst with the reassurance: "We'll cross that bridge when we get there!" We ended up having tinned peaches and slightly soured cream for dessert. My visions of a decadent chocolate dream-mousse dissipated when I saw the orange half-moons drifting in the transparent cough syrup-like substance. Nevertheless, compared to my month of culinary deprivation in hospital, this was a feast.

For Ma

Your hands on the steering wheel
have oddly changed?
Changed – like peeled apples
without lemon –
overnight.
I look again . . .
You're pretty
with your eyes
the hue of
a loquat's heart
and your fig-milk laugh.
Your hands are older now;
the peel of ripe quinces.
Hands that speak of
fruit salad-making
of sweet and bitter.

And they are soft
on my cheek
like the taste of a peach
on the first day
of the new season.

For a few months I spent my life pottering around the house, watching the leaves fall and the grass grow.

One of my wishes had always been not to lead a treadmill existence, not to become a creature of habit, caught up in the rat race.

Now I swore I would do anything for that to happen for me. Now, being normal seemed to me the ultimate aim in life. My movement or lack thereof was a far cry from the accepted understanding of the term and my handwriting left much to be desired. In fact, it was painstakingly slow and I often could not even decipher my own writing.

I felt that thinking of myself as less than perfect would be destructive. So I thought of altering my interpretation of "perfection" to reflect my new conviction. I didn't want to think of myself and others in these rigid terms. It would create a flat and impotent world. I had preconceived notions of what it meant to be perfect. If I continued to worship the concept, I would always be oblivious to the rich variety of life around me.

I began to understand that if I embraced my illness, tried to see the beauty and perfection in my broken body, my crutches, my walking aid, my wheelchair, and in the countless falls when I would collapse like a sack of flour on the floor, this would seed a new and more fulfilling kind of life.

True to my new resolution, I decided to try and play the piano again after a long period of silence. A copy of Mozart's "Fantasia" lay on top of the piano. It was the last piece that I had played. When I was sixteen, I tried for many months to master the fine co-ordination that was essential to the piece. One day, after failing to perfect the quick escalating scales, I banged the piano shut and vowed never to touch it again. Here I was again, four years later, hesitantly trying to caress the old instrument again. So much had happened in the meantime. Maybe the tumultuous love-hate relationship was long forgotten. Memories started to flood my mind. Throughout my life I had an intense relationship with the piano. Now I had to rethink my attitude towards it.

It was difficult to change my perception. For a whole four years I had refused to touch a piano. I couldn't straighten my broken leg and was confined to the hospital's Green Cross wheelchair, but I awkwardly wheeled myself into position. I did not desperately ache to succeed; instead, I wanted to try and find it pleasant. But my fingers were rigid and remained so, even after several months of attempting to warm them up. I was forced to resort to simplified versions of the complex pieces that I had played only four years before: Grieg's "Impromptu in B Flat Major" and Schumann's "Knight Rupert". Again I wanted to refrain from labelling my playing as imperfect. Instead, I enjoyed imagining myself as the disembodied pianist playing concertos amongst the stars.

Attempting life as I knew it

Moon dancer
(For Malcolm)

You sat under the stars
in your wheelchair
on the porch,
startled
by the heavenly bounty.
Your emaciated body
a denunciation by God.
The moon glanced down at you;
part of God's perfidy.

But your eyes
luminous
and brilliant; your stoicism
did not know dejection.
The wisdom in your eyes
proclaimed loudly
that you absolved yourself
and broke the manacles
of guilt.

"Life has a way of sorting itself out," my gran used to say. Malcolm's life was taking shape. Together with a friend, he founded a dance group, Remix, which is a roaring success. Their offices are based at UCT and they have several full-time employees. They focus on dancing as an art form as opposed to a means of therapy. The group involves people of all abilities. People from all walks (or non-walks) of life are involved: disabled, non-disabled, seers, non-seers, hearers, non-hearers. Remix gives them the freedom to be their own spokespeople through movement.

Malcolm dancing with a partner

The dance form isn't prescriptive, it is fluid; seaweed. It doesn't depend on reliable, sturdy legs. It doesn't respond to regimentation. It has no stringent modus operandi. It is not cast in stone. It does not thrive in a box. It is not watertight or compartmentalised. It cannot be circumscribed.

It's ideal for the body with ataxia that desires to shriek up high in the branches of a weeping willow. It embraces every form of life, every tiny movement. It is impulsive, unpredictable, adopts a laissez-faire approach, allows for carte blanche. It accepts, absorbs and integrates

Being pushed by a friend, Valerie Bailly

light. It swells with humanity, bursting at the seams. It asks for one thing only: it wants to breathe.

After the accident I knew that watching leaves falling for a few months is one thing, but spending my whole life doing it was out of the question. I knew that my survival depended on keeping myself moving. As I became progressively bored, I decided to resume my second year of studies – this time at the University of Cape Town.

At first, as I wheeled myself across campus, I attracted a dispro-portionate share of student healers from bizarre religious sects. It was difficult enough to be the odd one out and to be acutely aware of my inability to manoeuvre a wheelchair. I felt even more alien-ated when unknown individuals besieged me and fervently started to pray for me while they had no clue as to who I was, where I came from and what my spiritual preferences were. These episodes made me feel as if I were lying naked on an operating table under fluores-cent lights with gleaming eyes examining every part of me.

My first day at university is imprinted on my mind. Hundreds of students were milling around all along University Avenue. My head made a buzzing sound and my heart started throbbing in my throat. I felt eyes boring into me and clamped my jaw. Being confronted by hundreds of people cramped into such a small space, was frightening.

A solitary man sat on the periphery of the crowds. His head was shaved and he had a pair of tiny Charlie Chaplin spectacles perched on his nose. I parked myself under the tree that he had claimed for himself and took out my sandwiches. The tree was a sorry substitute for the loquat tree of my Grahamstown days, but it provided enough shade against the heat that was already beginning to pick up. As I started to eat my first sandwich, I heard a strange humming sound: "Hmmmmm, ohmmmmmm." Surely, mosquitoes never made their appearance during the day? The funny sound came from the Charlie Chaplin character. He looked up apologetically. "Just doing my breathing techniques." For lack of any appropriate response, I offered him one of my sandwiches. I was filled with astonishment that a normal-looking person, not obviously dying of pneumonia, felt a need to practise his breathing. I could think of a million better things to do. "No thanks," he managed to utter in-between the breaths: "I'm just focusing on attaining peace of mind for the day."

Well, I thought, thanks for that piece of your mind. "You see," he said, "Buddha taught the principle of the four noble truths. In layman's terms they are: a) There is struggle, b) Struggle has a reason, c) Struggle eventually ends, and d) There is a pathway to freedom . . ."

I thought to myself that it had to be impossible to cross the pathway to freedom in a wheelchair. In my case, it was unquestionably a contradiction in terms!

I thought of a poem by Yeats I'd recently read from the magic jewellery box that my mom had given me in Grahamstown and which had accompanied me all these years. The end of it will always be etched in my mind:

"I would spread the cloths under your feet:
But I, being poor, have only my dreams;
I have spread my dreams under your feet;
Tread softly because you tread on my dreams."

I wondered how different my life would be if the imprints I left behind me on this earth weren't two straight lines from the wheels of my chair, but those made by the soles of my feet? Oh, how I wanted to tread softly on my loved ones' dreams.

Charlie Chaplin was muttering something about the Chinese destroying the rights of his Tibetan brothers and sisters. I gathered that he meant the "brothers and sisters" thing metaphorically, because he was as white as lamb's wool, with glowing red cheeks reflecting his angst – a direct British import! I tried to smile compassionately. "But you know," he said, "I should always remember that the ultimate source of my strength is my peace of mind. No external turmoil can even cause a ripple on the sea of . . ."

Before he could complete his sentence, a strange man came up to me and placed his hand on my forehead. Taken aback, I reversed the wheelchair towards the trunk of the tree, but he wasn't fazed and kept advancing. His hand felt like a hot iron burning a hole into my forehead. Without any introduction, he plunged into a frenzy of verbal diarrhoea: "I, Jonathan Brown, free this enslaved child from all evil spirits, demons and unclean entities." As he spoke his voice rose steadily so that the amorphous mass of students around us grew silent and turned their collective gaze on the strange scene being played out before them. I was flustered, and glancing nervously around me, I felt my whole body stiffen.

His voice grew into more of a crescendo: "Every day, I help many students out of their dens of iniquity. Therefore, I demand those spirits that entice, torment and harass this defiled and manacled body, to leave it at once!" And with froth gathering at the corners of his mouth, he threw his arm up in the air. He was a bird of carrion sweeping down on its prey, tearing at its flesh, bit by bit. People were starting to gather around us. I fervently hoped that he had reached the end, but he continued in a tense, simmering tone of voice: "I warn thee, repent of all sins. Break with the occult and freemasonry." His voice was high-pitched: "Sever all these evil doings and, above all, resist the devil. Submit to . . ."

Suddenly Charlie Chaplin stepped in between us and said firmly: "Leave her alone, buddy, she's had enough!" He started pushing the wheelchair away from the whispering crowd of students, and, as he did so, Jonathan Brown disappeared into the throng. I was infinitely thankful to Charlie, a virtual stranger, who probably felt obliged to help after our brief chat. In silence, we made our way to the cafeteria.

There were steps leading up to it and I could already see a "damsel in distress / knight in shining armour" scenario developing, with him picking me up and carrying me over the threshold of the cafeteria. He could easily have done it, because he was a big, strong man, in fact, the little round spectacles looked rather silly above his strong jaw. But thanks be to the gods, there was a ramp on the side of the building. We sat at a table in the corner, strategically chosen to avoid any further limelight. He introduced himself to me: "Hi, I'm Liam. No relation to the actor."

So, not Charlie after all.

"Hi, nice to meet you. My name's Marguerite Black, Margs for short. Well, that was a dose of religion, strong enough to last me a lifetime!"

"If you ask me, strong enough to kill an ox!"

We vented our pent-up feelings by giggling like two teens.

"Between your Buddhism and Johnny 'The Freak', I could reach fully-fledged sainthood!" I joked.

We started drinking our cheap student coffee and he lit a cigarette, again putting on his "guru face".

"Someone who almost did reach sainthood was Gandhi. I respect the man a lot. He could just mutter a few things between parched lips and change the whole course of India's political history. With his slight figure of only 95 pounds and clothed only in a flimsy loincloth and a blanket, he made a permanent imprint on this earth."

"Yes, yes, beyond a doubt. But please don't, when I see you again, pitch up in a loincloth and blanket!"

He asked softly: "Hope you don't mind me asking . . . why is it that you can't walk?"

I gave him the bare outlines of Friedreich's ataxia.

He nodded and faintly smiled: "Well, we'll call it Fred's from now on . . . you know, we can think of Fred as our constant companion . . ."

I laughed: "Yeah, maybe we can form the world's most unusual threesome!"

Liam and I became great pals for the next two years. And Fred never left our sides.

After Liam had left that day, I remained sitting at the table and thought with wonder about how the right people always appeared at the right time. The next moment Lesley, a friend of my mother's, came to join me. She was studying psychology with me and had offered to help me get through the year. She gave me lifts in the mornings and afternoons, offered to get me books at the library and pep talked me through the remainder of my second year. She was a tutelary angel and at forty-something she fitted right into student life with her trendy clothes and beaming smile.

As spring proceeded into summer, I graduated from wheelchair to walking aid. I still felt weary and tired after each day, my body twisted and knotted from the physical effort of getting around the campus in the wheelchair. It felt as if I'd been moulded into the chair and I often had a horrible vision of my body and the chair merging into one.

I would drag my tired body into an upright position, frantically clinging to the frame before me, my body screaming dissent at the change of posture. Then I would give myself time to adjust to the higher altitude – the new vantage point made me feel dizzy and disorientated.

During these attempts to walk again, my mind often wandered – a dangerous act which could distract me from paying my undivided attention to the painstaking task at hand, the tricky art of walking.

Once I was thinking about how nice it would be to fix myself a cup of coffee. The verb "fixing" was such an inappropriate and ironic word to use in my case. I could never just do something on the spur of the moment. Everything had to be carefully premeditated. Words like "fixing" had to be ruthlessly banned from my vocabulary. Apart from coffee-making being a laborious and slow process, it was decidedly dangerous and unwise to hold a cup of steaming liquid in an unsteady hand.

Often, I had to bring back my thoughts to the business at hand; adopt tunnel vision and discard the possibility of peripheral sight. I placed one foot carefully in front of the other, trying to establish a pattern of "heel first, tip of toe last". But the logical rhythm that I so meticulously planned, would change into a crazy off-beat bossa nova every time. The legs jerking violently into a locked position without giving the muscles a chance to do their work and the feet dragging themselves, painfully scratching the sides. I felt totally disconnected from the bottom half of my body.

It was during this time, at the age of twenty-one, that I first went to see a natural healer.

I think my problem with conventional "solutions" probably goes back to my childhood. In Grahamstown, my mom sometimes took us to church on Sundays. The church was an ugly yellow brick building, the epitome of Fifties architecture, on the other side of town. I'm not sure whether it could be classified as a house of God, perhaps a military base would be a more appropriate description for it. The church focused solely on the punitive aspects of the Bible and

Walking on the beach in Hermanus with my cousins, Danielle and Hantie Barrie

it seemed to me that every preacher who set foot in that church was busy perfecting the art of pointing his finger at the congregation. I used to think, every time the preacher lashed his sharp tongue over the flock, that the angels in heaven forgot their chorus lines.

I was also taken to the Sunday school on a few occasions, but got cold feet after having forgotten my collection money one too many times. Mrs Ravenscroft would glare at me: "Do not tempt the Lord, girl! Our Lord's wrath can flare up and lick the skin off your baby-soft bottom!" After that I never set foot in the place again and wished that I could join Miriam at her Church of the Merciful Lord in the township. Every Sunday the church was jam-packed and there was no end to the singing and dancing. People bumped their hips against each other and hallelujahed till the cows came home. The preacher's zealous Praise the Lord's burst open like pomegranates and would have made even the staunchest atheist convert without a second thought.

Sundays I would sit with my mother under the Jerusalem thorn tree in the front garden, listening to her saying thanks for the golden bug that caught her eye and showed her the way to the heart of a rose, for the weaver bird who wove its ingenious house on the river bank, or for the shongololo that could coil itself up in a split second, pretending to be lifeless. Whenever I saw a shongololo making its way up a tree trunk, it seemed to wink at me with its glassy eyes. Since I was small, I would shudder at these strange creatures with their hundreds of legs, the same shiny black colour as the Marmite spread I ate on my bread. My mom's belief didn't force or push or shove you. It was gentle, like a warm breeze coming from the hill on summer evenings. She never stifled herself in litanies of rules and prescriptions, she could fly up high with the swallows and sing with the cicadas.

Here I was then, many years later, on the verge of being a grown-up, trying to make sense of life in a very different way. I was looking up at the healer's dream catchers, from countless unknown tribes across the globe (or so he told me).

He plunged into persuasive chatter. I soaked up his enthusiasm and his optimistic take on my life: "My girl, listen carefully. One can transcend one's physical reality through the imagination . . . Marguerite, do not resist the illness and view it as that disagreeable upset along the way, but as the very route on which you could tread towards wholeness."

I promised the healer that I would always be aware of the power of affirmations, of telling myself that I'm beautiful and strong, have the potential to get better, will get better and that my legs will carry me. I forced myself to say to myself: "I will have perfect balance. I am in touch with my body. My body is not well right now and needs my love and care. I promise to be gentle, tender, loving and soft with myself."

After the visit, I felt quite buoyant as I went down the hillside towards the car. I had never thought of the condition as "that disagreeable upset", though ataxia eclipsed so much of my life.

On another occasion, he told me: "You know, Margs, hyper-sensitive people get these kinds of conditions, but it is possible to reprogramme the body." With great urgency, he continued: "Your cells have to know there's another way. Since the onset of the condition, your body has been hurt so many times that it has gone into a state of shock and reacted like an injured bird." He hunched his shoulders as if imitating a hurt animal.

There was some truth in what he was saying. Ever since the accident, my body seemed to cry out for sleep and was at its happiest enveloped by blankets. I was like the chick of the masked weaver, blind and naked, afraid to leave the nest. My body seemed shy of the light and scared of the waking world around it. And then the rude reminder, the realization that during the early hours of the morning, I was like any other person – lying in bed, lulled by sleep, wrapping up my dream for the night. The next moment, I would have to surrender to the truth and drag my tired body onto the chair, struggle to get my clothes on, try to make breakfast – it all took painstaking concentration.

During my next visit, he continued dramatically, gesticulating with his arms: "Talk to your cells, Marguerite, so that they will be soothed and vibrate at a more normal frequency." There was a long pause, thrown in for extra effect. Since he first told me that, I thought irritably, I'd tried every conceivable kind of talk in every possible nuanced tone of voice. I tried smooth talking, small talk, baby talk, every single pick-up line, soft talk, hard talk: no response. There was a huge communication block as high as Mount Sinai itself.

He gave me little mantras to say regularly so that I could keep myself sane, e.g., "I am perfect for where I am in my evolutionary process. I would not have this if I couldn't cope with it. I am ready to cope with this." Another time, he said: "Be present in the here and now. Do not pour your emotions into past memories or future dreams." The audacity of that healer! Was he trying to con me into believing that a constant emotional high would make everything okay? Or that living in an illusion would numb the pain of my reality? I wasn't interested in anything artificial, false emptiness. I wanted truth. No straight poker faces – the raw truth. I wanted to shout: "Here I am, standing bare and exposed in the fluorescence of God's spotlight. I want the truth!"

Still, I did say his mantras and they did help to carry me through that time.

Back at home, I would think to myself: When I walk with this metallic frame, it is tough and jarring. I've had to invest my undivided attention into trying to make my legs move alternately and correctly. I wish I could allow the air to play with my skin. But it is as if the stiff and rigid motion smothers all other sensation. Sometimes having to concentrate so much makes my head hum so that everything else is shut out . . . I don't see or feel anything, especially not myself or the space surrounding me.

I started to attempt the pilgrim's progress from one side of the campus to the other with my walking aid. At first people craned their necks when they encountered me, inching my way across campus, but as the novelty wore off they greeted me with encouraging smiles. When I reached the other side, I would feel a surge of relief and an intoxicating sense of accomplishment.

Standing in a shopping centre

Freedom – found and lost

When I was twenty-two, I decided that it would be nice to be able to drive. My determination to lead a full life in spite of a physical restriction meant that I often ventured into the world of mechanics. My first introduction to this hitherto unknown territory occurred at this time. My grandpa's 1978 Mercedes cum chicken coop had been standing in our yard since time immemorial. Weeds with razor-sharp leaves were sprouting from the tyres. I decided to fix up the old wreck and get my licence. A friend of my parents, Uncle George, a farmer from the Worcester area and a staunch believer in the fix-it-yourself school of thought, was my partner in crime. We gave the car a complete make-over and transformed it into a respectable means of transport. We even fitted it out with hand controls so that I would only have to use my arms to manoeuvre the army tank. I seriously had to suspend disbelief that it was remotely possible to budge the monstrous thing in this way. But what do you know – abracadabra – it worked beautifully! It was pure joy to turn up my speed levels by so many notches. To this day, the novelty hasn't worn off.

It dawned on me: with my "new" car I wouldn't only be able to easily visit friends, but to get from Cape Town to the Orange River in the south of Namibia – another country entirely – in two days. And that is exactly what I did!

I had obtained my licence three months earlier and had an overwhelming desire to put my new-found freedom to the test. I had had an amazingly placid driving instructor. Her demeanour had a contagious effect on me. She never stopped me abruptly or shouted out in an alarming way. She sat next to me like a meditating Buddha, not batting an eyelid when the palookas on the road started to gesticulate wildly and to slam on their brakes at every robot when they caught a glimpse of me. It felt as if she had sedated me. She even coaxed me into driving over Chapman's Peak in my second week of lessons. I wasn't in the least fazed by the dizzying heights. It was as if I was sleepwalking over the pass.

For this reason, the trip up north to the Orange River seemed like no big deal.

A few months earlier I had met a Dutch girl, Martine (Tine), at university. We became the best of friends. She was always radiant, bouncing with energy and at least two feet taller than the average student. Many wonderful things could be said about the no-nonsense, fun-loving Martine. But no description could really do justice to the warmth of her personality.

A few things could not be said of her:

a) that she was politically correct. She jokingly called me an ataxian (sounding like Martian). That put paid to any discomfort between us concerning "the condition".

b) that she had airs. She was vehemently candid about everything and was not in the least pretentious: she hated the way in which many people treat people with physical difficulties. She never treated me as if I were precious like a Fabergé egg. She expressed her thoughts in a raw and uncensored way. When she first encountered our dog, a docile and benevolent golden Labrador, she shrieked in horror: "Shut up, dog, shut up . . . (Normally she was very eloquent, but she couldn't speak fluent English when she was cross.) . . . stay away from me. I don't like dogs spitting all over me!" To her, all pets were like irritating mosquitoes. And insects she referred to as "animals". When a fly bothered her she would say: "Get this stupid animal off me." And anyone in the near vicinity would burst out laughing. Of course, this would make her even more annoyed.

With Tine, I went up to the Orange River to do river rafting with a whole group of tourists. The ancient white Mercedes, our personal *QE2*, managed to transport us safely up country and back home. It was not a luxurious trip. The torn seats and lack of air conditioning didn't exactly make for comfortable travelling and from sitting in a tense, upright position for hours on end, my feet quickly became red and swollen.

Martine, who had her learner's licence, offered to drive half of the way. But when she started to drive, refusing to exceed 60 km/h on the national roads, I kindly declined when she next offered and she was forced to accept my role as sole driver. On our way, we passed peculiar little towns, unaltered by the passage of time. The first of these was Garies where the unsavoury looking pool bar was the social hot spot of the town. Not far from Garies, we stopped in Kamieskroon, a bewitching little place perched on koppies in the clouds. It was as if the town had stepped out of another era. A Mazawattee-tea advert from the Fifties embellished the walls of the corner café. It sported a radiant housewife in a neatly ironed morning dress with hair teased up in a beehive. She was serving tea to her picture-perfect family. Our next stop was Vanrhynsdorp. The ambience reflected a feeling of post-Sunday-lunch lethargy. We had pancakes with cinnamon sugar and lemon, and feeling lazier than ever, literally had to drag ourselves back to the car. The intoxicating effect of being self-sufficient lessened as we made our way up to the national road. As we approached

Namibia, the landscape became more and more alien, dotted with succulents, stretching out their fleshy leaves to the blue heavens.

On my trip down the Orange River, I didn't have to lift a finger. I lounged in the back of a two-man canoe with one of the guides taking charge. I was rowed down the river by a tanned Orange River Viking. The camp sites along the river didn't come with any bathroom conveniences. So, every time I needed to disappear behind a bush up the hill, the whole group was alerted: "Margs is using the toilet. Stay clear!" Two people would walk on either side of me up the hill and leave me behind the bush for five minutes. Gone were the days of discreetly whispering: "I'll be back in a second . . ."

Tine and I could talk and talk. After a few months of knowing each other, we decided to go to Lesotho to ride ponies during the

Martine and I

December holidays. We had tasted freedom on our trip to Namibia and were keen to spread our wings further. It was wonderful to be encapsulated in a car with each other's company for hours on end. This time, she was doing the driving and I could sit back and relax. At one point, she asked me what it was like to have ataxia. I thought for a long time: "It is relentless; a downward spiral. I had a needle-work teacher when I was in primary school. She always made me undo my flimsy knitting. When I realised that I had ataxia, it was as if she had made a reappearance . . . Ever since, she's been unravelling the careful knitting of my life."

She said: "Why don't you write about it, Magriet. I have kept a diary since a young age. I think writers should be allowed to write about themselves. That's the only way in which to be authentic and honest."

I thought for a while: "If I were to do reams and reams of writing or gallery upon gallery of oils (not that I can paint), it won't explain what I feel. At this stage I can only laugh about it. You know all about my spurts of hysterical laughter, Tine. It is the only way I can express my incomprehension at such a cruel thing. Maybe laughter is as sane a response as crying. No reaction could ever really soften it."

"Well, maybe you are doing the right thing," Martine said. "You know the saying: 'Smile and the world smiles with you' . . ."

But I was quick to disagree: "That isn't really the reason why I do it. It just starts . . . It just happens."

Martine said lightly: "Perhaps it has to do with the cycle of the moon and its phases. You should have been Luna Black!"

It was good to speak my mind: "You know, I frantically try to preserve myself, try to cling to the familiar; and I want to refuse to accept that life eventually wilts. But I guess it's inevitable. Maybe it's the survival instinct that takes over. I see it in my own body. The deterioration just spurs me on to keep on moving – even if it's almost impossible. I was in denial for six years. I wish I still were. Now, I want to fight it till the very end."

"But you do fight it, Magriet. If you make it part of your life, you are defeating its purpose. It wants you to fight with your body. But your body doesn't stand much of a chance. You deceive it by fighting it with your mind and with your tongue that speaks of the things that it does to your body. You will remember and recollect. This is your weapon, Magriet. Don't forget that."

I laughed tiredly: "It's strange to think of myself as armed in any way. I feel so completely defeated."

"In flesh, Magriet, not in spirit," she said adamantly. "Mark my words."

"These days, when I go to the corner café near our house with my walker to buy bread, I'm always singled out. People smile at me pityingly, ask me outright what happened to me. We're talking about buying bread! The simple act of buying bread, Tine!"

Martine smiled: "Of course! I can imagine that you just want to blend in!"

I was always surprised at how she knew exactly how I felt, as if she knew how my thought processes worked.

"It's like being the perpetual intruder of the neighborhood, the victim of circumstances. Even when I put on my red silk Chinese shoes and dye my hair bottle blonde, people pat me encouragingly on the shoulder."

"I feel just as lost as you," Martine sighed. "I keep pestering myself with impossible questions, asking myself: 'Who am I? Why did I come to this earth and what is my life's purpose?' But then I remind myself that I need to live my whole life before I can answer that. I am so adaptable and . . . as elusive to myself . . . you know . . . as wet soap in a child's hand."

"I understand you, Tine," I replied, "you don't have to be anything else than you are at this moment."

I remember her adding knowingly: "Now that I'm older, I keep on reminding myself of an old proverb – when you see a fork in the road, choose the difficult path. Sometimes I wish I could be small again," Martine said, "when things were simple . . ."

"Yes, me too. I yearn for Grahamstown – the mountainside and sharp-billed honeybirds; the grass shimmering in the hazy afternoon heat. I long for the days that I could sit under the gnarled trunk by the water's edge, beading necklaces from the seeds of an agapanthus. That place has crept under my skin – for good . . ."

We seemed to be contained within the same thought-bubble, feeling glowingly happy, driving through the summer landscape of long grass and pink cosmos flowers.

What exactly happened after that, I do not know. Perhaps Tine, being from Europe, became confused between the right and left side of the road. The full story was told to me by rescue workers and medical staff. One and a half hours from Jo'burg, we were involved in a head-on collision. Afterwards, I was overwhelmed by a litany of factual information that I've tried to glue together in a coherent way. But it remains surreal and disjointed. The story refuses to settle in the archive of past experience. How could everything be reduced to a car wreck?

A while after the moment of impact, I opened my eyes. Tine lay on my lap. She was at peace; from one moment to the next, my animated friend had become a waxen doll. I drifted off again. I heard two men, trying to cut loose our seatbelts. One was saying: "Is she still alive?" The other one, bending over Tine, said: "I can't feel a pulse." The first man said: "And the other one?" I managed to whisper: "I'm alive . . ."

I lost consciousness, only remembering fragments: the helicopter; rescue workers saying urgently: "Be careful, she has ataxia"; my dad running towards the helicopter as it landed, repeating tearfully: "I love you, Jolie, I love you . . ." I fell into a deep sleep that lasted for days, momentarily awaking to stare impotently at images from *The Jungle Book* that had been painted on the ceiling of the ICU.

The doctors suspected internal injuries, but in the end it turned out that I had only been badly bruised. My dad brought me a shiny green puppet with a harlequin hat, but nothing could stop the thoughts: "Why did I survive? I was the one with ataxia. There must have been a mistake . . ."

The firefly

Martine, you haven't died.
You are the sugarbird in the flame tree.
You are the light that dances on the mountain stream.
Your laughter is the waterfall under the dragonfly.
Your silences are smoke-blue mountains in the morning,
early.

Martine, you haven't died.
On the rock face are your gestures
and you talk to me.
You are the mongoose that peeks around rocks.
Also the cobra that rustles in the leaves.

But I am like a child
who wants to catch the firefly
when the light and dark mix at dusk
– and I hear you calling in the night wind.

Catching my breath

I was twenty-three when I met Benjamin Roux at a restaurant. He is the son of wonderful family friends of my parents and was studying Fine Arts, Classics and Philosophy at the University of Cape Town. I will always think of him as a delicate being; an exotic creature. As I was walking painfully slowly with the walking aid, he looked concerned and gently asked me: "Does it hurt when you walk?" A strong recognition welled up in me, and I know now that the privilege of getting to know him is one of the reasons I have survived.

On our first date together we drove to a little town near Cape Town and had a picnic by a dam. We sat quietly next to each other, suspended in the silence, in a vacuum without time. After what must have been almost an hour, we were startled by a powder-blue turtledove singing a soft, warbling song from within the branches of a wild olive. Ben looked up at me with his complex eyes and traced his finger up the inside of my arm. It was white like the belly of an amphibious animal, thin blue veins mapping the surface under the skin. I felt deeply self-conscious and tried to avoid his eyes, looking away and blushing at a hammerhead admiring its strange head in the murky water. Its backwards-facing crest made it look self-righteous and impudent.

I wanted to be swallowed by the earth beneath me and started fumbling through my muddled thoughts for something to say. I couldn't think straight. At last I managed to say awkwardly, stumbling over the words: "The vanity of that bird makes me think of something I heard somewhere . . . uhhm, there are two types of women – the one type merely dresses up for the sheer reason of showing off. Uhhm, and the other type dresses up because of a love for the beautiful and the way in which it enhances her figure."

How could I have said such a stupid thing? This made me feel even more self-conscious. He still tickled the inside of my arm with his finger and continued up to my neck. A sudden shudder stole

Ben and I at a wedding

93

through my whole body and I was filled with elation. A malachite kingfisher swirled in the air above us and my body felt weightless and free, maybe a seraphim was hovering above my head, pulling me up to the highest cloud by a silver thread.

We must have spent the whole night by the dam, our conversations flowing into one another, without beginning or end. A silvery dawn was lifting the darkness without our noticing, and we became aware of the waking world around the dam.

Shortly after we met, in November 2001, we went on a diving course in Mozambique. I was excited to try a new form of swimming.

Apart from the hellish swimming lessons in Grahamstown, I generally love swimming. In water, I can let go of my rigid, defensive muscles and succumb to the soft liquid moulding itself around my body. In water, I've never hurt myself. I can trust it completely. It is my link to sanity.

I was once told the story of the seal whose skin was stolen by a human; without a skin, she was forced to become a wife on the land. She could not live there, her body was dying. She wanted to break free from the manacles of gravity and yearned for the place of her origin, where she belonged, to soften the ache in her heart, the madness in her step. I am like her; without a skin, burnt by the sun above the soil that keeps me captive. When I drift in the water, I return to my roots.

Yet, my diving trip in Mozambique was a slightly different story. One thing that I've learnt is never to be too sure of anything. As luck would have it, I slipped on the bathroom floor the night before the course started. I was washing my hair over the side of the bath, lost my balance and crashed against the wall. There was a deep gash in my head. Although I couldn't see it, I imagined it to be the width and depth of the Fish River canyon. I tried to smother my cries, so as not to embarrass Ben, but I don't think I succeeded. There was no hospital in Ponto do Ouro, in the southern part of the country, so we had to endure another bumpy ride in a Land Rover across the border to Monguzi, the closest town in KwaZulu Natal. I waited for hours in queues of despondent people, in corridors where cockroaches scurried across the floor. Rudimentary facilities and a lack of staff meant that I had to wait for the best (or worst) part of the day. My panic increased when I found out that not only did I need stitches, but also a tetanus injection – an antidote to the bacteria-infested water. In a typical stint of stubbornness, a trait that has been entrenched in me since birth, I got up at the crack of dawn the next morning to be ready for the diving course. But the drama hadn't even begun yet. After practising in a swimming pool for one hour, we got kicked out. Our instructor hadn't paid her fees. This meant that we were thrown into the sea – twelve metres under the water – on our second day. We didn't even quite know how to read our meters, let alone how to equalise and do mask lifts. It was literally sink or swim. To top it all, I couldn't get the weights around my body to balance, with the result that I couldn't even get past the first baby step – sinking. By the time the rest of the group came up to the surface after their dive, I started my descent, feeling very sheepish. I was left by my lonesome self at the bottom of the sea, trying to survive, hardly noticing any morsel of aquatic life. However, this rather terrifying experience did not cure me of my adventurous streak.

In December 2001, I became fascinated by all sorts of charismatic religions. Perhaps there was a direct link between this behaviour and the diving nightmare? My naivety made me an especially malleable subject. A few times, I visited a place of healing. The "Men of God" tried to exorcise me by placing their creepy hands on my head and instructing the "evil spirit" of the "disease" to leave my body. They encouraged me to express any spontaneous action that might arise during these episodes such as vomiting, screaming or falling over. To their disappointment, I was a pale and unexciting candidate who just stood there with eyes as round as saucers, showing no sign of improvement over the course of seven healing services. The twelve "Men of God" had very solemn expressions on their faces and as the treatment progressed they started to look more and more like praying mantises that were closing in on me with their wriggling feelers. They kept telling me to believe like a child and, for a while, I focused intensely on suspending disbelief and regressing to the thought-processes of a child. In fact, I wanted it so desperately, that I were prepared to return to the womb. But I just wouldn't get healed. While the sick ones around me were exulting that their cells were being renewed by the Holy Spirit, I was left feeling incompetent – as if I were just not trying hard enough. Was it possible to undo the intricate map of the mind and to erase most of it? For seven sessions the praying mantises were screaming hysterically at "the demon" inside of me to get out. It was as if they were pretending to draw it out by their own physical magnetic forces. It was sheer exhibitionism, a rush for the exorcists who claimed to offer a quick fix for each and every ailment. The limelight that these services offered to the praying mantises was the very best space in which to close in on their unsuspecting prey.

It was during this time that I realised my mind was still filled with confusion and other harming emotions about myself. It was as if my being was entangled in the undergrowth of a forest, a state that was almost more damaging than my physical one.

At the age of twenty-four, I was still studying, doing my MA in Creative Writing at the University of Cape Town. Since the age of six I had never stopped being a student. I loved this life of perpetual studying.

I needed to breathe and I felt that I could perhaps take my first gulp of fresh air by channelling the confusion in a creative way. I still had so much to learn.

I just had to look at my brother Malcolm to see how to be creative, successful and true to oneself. Malcolm explored countless areas of study – Engineering, Psychology, IT, Art – before finding his niche: assisting in establishing the Remix dance group. Malcolm's talent in communicating with people and his sense of humour, have helped to unify this group of diverse individuals.

I gradually began to emerge from an eggshell. I had imagined myself into the past, because I tried (and still have to try continually) to join the dots between the dark, lonely and enigmatic labyrinth of this world and the world long gone. I began to get up at the break of dawn and would sometimes experience that feeling of the freedom of childhood: a time when I shrieked high up in the branches of the weeping willow by the dam on the hill in Grahamstown. And sometimes I would dream of an unbound body, then wake up, filled with the excitement of a child on Christmas morning. For a moment I would forget the difficulty and drift off to places far away . . . I promised to be gentle and kind to myself whenever I longed to make cartwheels in the garden of my childhood.

Visits to more physicians, natural healers, physiotherapists and prayer-sessions followed. At one time one of them realigned imbalances in my body, at another ten people stood around me, transmitting energy through their hands into my body. I remember this time as an initiation process or a rite of passage, and afterwards I felt as if I had been given a passport which said: *Marguerite, live your life as it was given to you.* After this message came through to me, I was propelled into my life again. I felt that if I had the courage to love myself and share

Swimming in a rock pool in the Cedarberg

it with others, I would have the courage for many other things.

Ben filled my life with enchantment, transforming it by his willingness to share. However, I still felt fenced in by the way a large part of my life was unfolding. I realised that wasn't going to change, but in acknowledging the transience of the body, I could nestle myself into a place that was my own, with the knowledge that there was endless space beyond the body in which to live. In some ways, limitations had set me free.

When I began to think that even a tiny movement can be like the journey of a thistledown, I chose to dance to the cries of the light and the rhymes of the shadows. I thought to myself: A fragile thing is beautiful, because it is vulnerable, fleeting and ephemeral. It is precious because it can disappear, break or change at any time. A soap bubble on the brink of being and non-being . . .

At a party with friends: from left – me, Roxanna Strong, Carine Phyffer, Mia Marx and Michelle du Plessis

For a long time I dwelled on the ephemeral nature of life. I worked for the Disability Unit at UCT as a research co-ordinator cum PR person cum book reviewer for two years. A large part of the job – the PR work – required of me to be objective, distant and businesslike when, in actual fact, I'm subjective, intimately involved and emotional about anything to do with perceptions of the body and physical difficulty.

As part of my work, I went in my wheelchair to visit the university's crèche. The kids literally swarmed around me, fascinated by this curiosity that had appeared out of thin air. As children often do, they talked to each other about me, never addressing me directly. One hollered at the top of her voice: "What is this?" Another one looked perplexed and offered an explanation: "it's some kind of bicycle." "No, silly," a chubby boy with ruddy cheeks interrupted, "it's a wheelchair."

Some of them looked dumbfounded. "A wheelchair?" A freckled boy with curly hair seemed to have a light bulb moment: "She had an accident!" They all gasped. A soft-spoken black girl with round spectacles stroked my arm and said as if to a kewpie doll: "Maybe she's ill." From the back of the group a little girl full of beans was jumping up and down, her blond plaits bobbing on her chest. She shrieked the conclusive answer: "You're all wrong. She's just lazy!"

I've recently taken to using an electric scooter that I had modified so that I can stand on it. A friend from the Mechanical Engineering Department, Horst, helped me with the alterations. From the very start, he was unbelievably uninhibited. After chatting to me a bit, he declared: "I always used to be afraid of people like you . . ."

I retorted: "And what kind of person may that be?" We both just laughed.

He introduced me to another student in a wheelchair, saying: "Meet your fellow inmate."

There was something refreshing about someone who didn't put a coat of sugar around things.

I love this new invention to bits. It feels zany to whiz past people in shopping malls and to be confronted by little boys, nagging their moms: "Mommy, Mommy, I also want one of those!" Pointing to the scooter, a girl once asked me: "Is that some kind of trendy accessory?" We laughed together and I said: "I guess you could say it's some sort of fashion statement." What I love about the scooter is the ambiguity of it. Normally, people are unsure what it's for. They cannot categorise me as one thing or the other, which makes the nomad in me hugely happy. Since I was a little girl I used to tell my parents: "Leave me alone. I can do it myself." Evidently, my character hasn't changed much over the years. The height of the scooter allows me to meet people on their level, use ATMs and interact with people over

Standing on my scooter

counters. I love the smooth floors of shopping malls simply because of the way in which the wheels of the scooter glide effortlessly over them.

All through the years, Frances and I never really spoke about the condition. She was the one who managed to dodge the genetic pitfall. I'd always felt protective of her and didn't want to involve her in a struggle that wasn't really hers.

Recently, for the first time, she came to me and spoke openly and lightly about the time that Malcolm and I started to struggle to walk. She told me how, when she was ten years old, two of her close friends asked her what was wrong with her brother and sister. She couldn't say anything and felt blind panic. She just looked at them blankly. The next moment, she turned around and ran away. She said: "Ever since I knew that you had ataxia, it's been such a threatening thing. But talking about it now, makes it easier ..."

I told her how I used to feel when I was younger: "I often felt like a non-entity, anonymous and small. I thought of myself as being in a glass cubicle, the untouchable, aware of the world mil-

Frances

ling around me, people actively talking and laughing with one another, brushing shoulders. And there I was, neatly tucked away in my glass box in the corner, trying to talk to someone, but not being heard; trying to make eye contact, but being avoided; trying to reach outside, but being quietly contained by glass walls."

We knew that, after a long time, we had reached each other.

Early one summer's morning, Ben and I revisited the dam where we had camped on one of our first outings together. One thing was sure – the constricting grip that I had felt for a long time was rapidly grow-ing weaker. A moorhen, immersed in the quickly warming shadows in the shrubs by the dam, was softly gurgling. The day lilies that grew by the water's edge were slowly revealing their slumbering petals. That morning I realised that I was gradually becoming my own spokesperson, carefully formulating and clarifying things for myself. Maybe that was one of the things that I had learnt from my friendship with Martine. If I had allowed the invasive poison of ataxia to eclipse even my love for others, I would have been forced into a state where it wouldn't have mattered to me whether I lived or died. I wouldn't have been able to summon enough strength to fight back; and the outcome of things would have been irrelevant to me. I felt lighter and had a first glimpse of the sun peeping over the shoulder of the hill. My mind was starting to become less nebulous and I thought of staking a claim to my own life. I wanted to make choices myself. Yes, I was penned up within the walls of ataxia. That was an unavoidable reality. But I could choose to watch the new day's sun emerging, or to suffocate in my shallow breath; I had the right to make that choice myself. I reminded myself what I whispered in the car wreck: "I am alive . . ."

Making meaning

During the December holidays of 2004, I went swimming with Ben in a tidal pool in Hermanus. A few years previously I could easily keep afloat. Now it wasn't possible any longer . . .

Swimming is a barometer by which I can witness my own body's deterioration or – sometimes – progress. It is a cruel reminder of the fact that Friedreich's ataxia is a slowly progressive disorder of the nervous system that proceeds from the nerve fibres to the cell bodies. Certain specific regions of the spinal cord and peripheral nerves are affected.

In the last two or three years I've been wearing a big flotation belt to stay afloat. No-one can call the belt flattering or trendy. It wouldn't even cross my mind to call it a fashion statement. The first time I wore it Ben said casually: "It doesn't look cool, Grieks." I tried not to look fazed and said in a no-nonsense tone of voice: "Rather safe than sorry," as I strapped the all-consuming blue thing around my waist. Ben said teasingly: "Okay, come, Monster!" He alternately calls me "My Love", "Grieks" and "Monster".

For many years, when I was a teenager and in my early twenties, I was disorientated, and I had to rewrite my whole personal code of meaning and start my life from scratch several times.

Life went on around me, but I was detached from it. I built defensive walls around me to shelter me from my physical reality and people's uncomprehending stares and insensitive remarks. In this way I could live in my past when I could climb the loquat tree, run to the hill, or go for a swim in the dam. I poured all my energy into the past instead of focusing on the present.

After the diagnosis, my anxiety at what was happening to me was transformed into anger, an anger that launched me into a duel with my body: a crude paradoxical view of myself versus ataxia. At that stage I didn't know that after a few years this way of living would require impossibly huge amounts of energy, and would destructively hammer away at my sense of self-worth. I didn't know that I was fighting a losing battle and that ultimately this anger would become detrimental to my growth. It never occurred to me that I had the choice to see the relentless pitfalls and potholes in my path as a difficult means to a meaningful end.

Today, I am beginning to understand that through living with this condition I have the opportunity to grow. In that sense, the experience of living with the condition is, in itself, a form of healing. It will take many more years for me to fully realise that. The most rewarding way in which to live is through accepting pain and embracing joy.

Illness need not be seen as a battle or struggle, but rather as a mentor or guide that straightens out the ruffles of our being on a purely physical level every moment of every day – it is a naked honesty that I share with the rest of the world: lights, action, camera – no time for stage fright! A friend once told me: "Marge, you've got centre stage! Use it, doll! Dye your hair purple. You go, girl!"

Although it is my instinct to resist the disorder, because it seems to have a fragmenting effect on all aspects of my life, I should rather follow its seemingly illogical path and reside in the knowledge that one day I will understand. Possibly there is a form of reasoning which directs a greater scheme of things. In the meantime I sometimes wonder whether the condition is an expression of a more complex truth from a deeper dimension. Illness and health, the two contrasting poles, are interactive, complementary and reciprocal, and both comprise wholeness.

Often I am entangled in a frantic search for meaning. At other times I meander and often think that the contemporary postmodern culture means that all the multiple truths eclipse my own, that I create a complicated tapestry of cluttered fabrications and become a tormented spirit in the process, weighed down by manacles of illusion. Of course this world is confusing precisely because it also affords others the chance to find their particular truths. In a world saturated with half-truths and thoughtlessness, my truth often plays hide-and-seek with me and teasingly eludes me. Maybe there is nothing to unveil and I should stop looking for profound answers and rather infantilise my thoughts. Perhaps my truth is humble and barefoot like a child who lies in straw in a basket, or is small like a mustard seed.

A child in a basket
a child in straw
the barefoot child
on the street corner
whose bewildered eyes
own the world
because they own
her being
because they own
her heart
when they look
they see

Sitting in the garden

I have an urge to put words into the void which surrounds ataxia. My writing is a way of saying: this is also important, because this is my truth. I have an overwhelming need to give voice to the smothered sounds of my life. I want to decipher myself and be understood. I've come to understand that many people who live in the shadows and on the margins have things to share and would like to speak out.

Was it a vision I had the other day? My grown-up self watched Malcolm and myself as children playing in our garden in Grahamstown. I could recognise the children, but felt estranged from them. They played like two mongooses, the pair of them; and I watched them intently, my eyes glued to the intoxication of it all: the hazy afternoon, the sun-baked children, quite contented with my just sitting there on the periphery, a new addition to their garden. Perhaps they got used to me, as I would imagine one would to a garden gnome or a water feature. I preferred it this way. I was used to being left alone, with my own thoughts. Their movements were lithe and agile as they cartwheeled and skipped all over the inclines. I felt a flicker of recognition of a time that seemed so long ago.

The children started to look at me after a while. Their movements became more tame and their shrieks died down. Their skin became the colour of the bark of the Jerusalem thorn tree. They came up to me, looking bewildered, each taking hold of one side of the wheelchair. We moved gingerly towards the hill and could not believe what we saw. The earth on the hill was jagged. Rivulets of dam water were flowing uphill towards the road. The sickly brown of the blood lilies looked intensely macabre. Natural laws were being violated. Everything looked lopsided. We wanted to flee the warped symmetry. The red-hot pokers flamed up more flamboyantly and the forest dragon trees flourished and seemed to duplicate by the minute. The crevices of rifts and canyons added to the eroded land. We plied the wheelchair over the rugged surface. I looked at the panoramic land behind me and saw the quick Mexican wave of brown replacing the sage green vegetation. We cringed and hurried back up to the road.

Malcolm-the-child let go of the wheelchair and started to run frantically, limbs flailing in all directions. We felt drained of all strength and tried to stop him, slowing down considerably. As we walked along, the mauve, fragile clusters of flowers of the doll's pow-der-puff wilted and browned. The sweet fragrance of the honeysuck-le turned acrid. In the last streaks of sunlight, we moved listlessly to a clearing in the grass by the side of the road, sank to the ground and sat amongst the blackened sedge flowers for a long, long time. At some point Malcolm-the-child came to join us.

My mother came up from the dam. A crescent moon was hover-ing above her head. She wandered slowly, thoughtfully, towards us in a dark, velvet garment. Her arms were full of lilies that she had picked down at the dam. She smiled at us tenderly while handing out the flowers. We all huddled closer together, waiting for the menacing chorus of hadedas to subside.

My older self reached out and spoke to the children: "Thank you for digging for roots of the bitter apple in the hard clay all through the summers of my youth. I will cherish the necklaces you made me: shiny coils, strung together out of the bright seeds of the orange flame lilies down by the railway line. Thank you for all the num-nums you gave me. I stuffed handfuls of them into my mouth, swal-lowing some of them whole. I ate till my stomach hurt."

My mother went to sit on her knees. She was silent for a long time. In her left hand, she held the thistledown from dandelions; three perfect spheres perched in the palm of her hand. She spoke very softly: "All of you, my children, young and old, make light."

She took a handful of red soil, gently sifting it through her fingers.

A goliath heron made a solitary descent into the weeping willow by the dam. It looked at us for a long time, unknowingly. I sat up in the wheelchair while glancing at the round web of thistledown in my hand. It quivered in the moving light. I blew the seeds and sent them into a pocket of air where they remained lingering for a while. The current picked them up and carried them to far-off places. I thought of loss, change, uncertain beginnings and of those who have to move on. A cold breeze stole through the undergrowth and once more we huddled closer together.

Afterword

My brother and I wrote a joint email, in an attempt to find some answers. Promising research is currently being conducted, but we sometimes feel as if it is a cloak-and-dagger business, and that we have to wrench answers out of the relevant role-players:

To whom it may concern: *November 2004*

At this point in time, it seems that things are definitely looking up concerning finding possible therapies for Friedreich's ataxia. My brother and I are hopeful about research in this area and wish to be considered for trials that aim to test the effects of developments in the frataxin enzyme and also stem cell treatment.

My brother is permanently in a wheelchair and I use a walking aid as well as a wheelchair. Yet, we are determined to find a way and try to be positive. We are more than willing to try any scientifically sound trials and experiments anywhere in the world and are prepared to take full responsibility for the outcome of such trials.

Up till now we haven't had positive answers and guidance regarding a possible cure, but we are very enthusiastic about the prospect of deriv-

ing benefit from any future trials. We would greatly appreciate working with you in this regard.

Kind regards and our sincere thanks,

Malcolm and Marguerite Black

We received brief, neutral responses to our letter and haven't, as yet, been able to bring about a pattern of regular correspondence. I remind myself not to put my life on hold while waiting for medical intervention. The seasons of my life still have to run their course. Thus far, we haven't had any concrete promises about potential trials that would be open to us, but we will continue fighting and hoping.

Fragile lives
by Louie Black

Life, to me, is filled with unanswered questions. How do I help Malcolm and Marguerite when their determination to stay independent seems to make it impossible to know what they need and what to do for them? More importantly, how can I make meaning out of life when a random condition eats away at my children's bodies, gnaws away at my children's frail lives? How can I, if I find such meaning, use it to give them hope and courage?

Over the years, among us, we have pocketed sensible-seeming religious and philosophical bits and pieces to be taken out when the need arises. I am aware that people who have a specific religious faith find solace in it, but to me God is unknowable; I do not see him as a father or as a friend, but simply as the inexplicable. But that the inexplicable is all around us, I have seen with awe. I have seen it when a beautiful dancer walks up to my son, who is being carried by friends at a concert, to ask him whether he would be interested in becoming her dance partner; thereby changing his life. I have seen it when a gentle young man and my daughter meet each other, look into one another's eyes and fall in love, and I have seen it in all the many friends who have simply appeared at the right moments, at different times, to be around us.

I have also seen it in the patterns of life and in the way that the past informs and sometimes haunts the present. I am grateful for the past and for the way in which I was brought up, which taught me to find joy in people and nature and ideas and books, and to be self-reliant and not too introspective. Introspection does not seem to me to be a useful activity. In spite of a whole culture of people absorbed by the need to know their inner selves, I absolutely do not want to be in contact with my deeper, sadder inner feelings. Such contact would incapacitate me. I would rather get stuck into work than think too deeply about the grief of the present and of the future.

The past is a much safer place for me and it sustains me still. Our home, when I was growing up, stood like a fortress of friendly activity. As I was a child then, life was arranged by other people and nothing much was expected of me except to go to school and to appear for supper. Pretoria in the Fifties and early Sixties was a rigid, fenced-in society. The sense of safety and security that we had was illusionary, but from our perspective it all seemed quite normal, predictable and extremely peaceful. At our house we were not even conscious of the fact that people were so divided that if they were of different races they did not shake one another's hands. We only knew what we saw at home, and in my mother's absent-minded way it probably never occurred to her to suspect that everybody else was not behaving as she was, running up, as she did, to well-loved black people and hugging and kissing them, all the while asking about their children and families.

In the garden that she nurtured a decades-old wisteria grew to the tips of the huge jacaranda tree and formed ropes which helped us children climb up to our tree house in which we spent much of our time playing and reading and in which we watched, close by, through the leaves, newly hatched baby birds being fed in their nests. A purple bougainvillea draped the length of a telephone pole. Insects drew patterns of light against the sky. In the backyard patches of shiny-leafed vegetables, along with the pergola on which we spent hours playing and eating grapes, formed the only formal patterns in a garden planted to attract butterflies and birds and in which fat lizards slithered away lazily at our approach. In the flowerbed to the side of the garden our little-girl faces looked up at the flowers of the dahlias which, in the summer season of late-afternoon thunderstorms, formed a dripping, spicily fragrant forest around us as the lightning receded over the horizon.

In those years, decades ago, my three siblings and I, like many of our contemporaries, were brought up on psychology learnt in the Thirties. Any hint of a psychological upset was dismissed as a stage and a complex that would disappear if ignored. They often did, but the child who had been classified as being the possessor of such a stage or complex was always left with a slightly cheated feeling of not owning his or her own emotions and of never being centre stage. In our case, how we felt was hardly contemplated at all while our mother chatted to us, read or arranged flowers, did some work for charities, quoted poetry and entertained guests. We, or at least those of us that way inclined (of which I was a prime specimen), could, while she was busy, run wild, go around barefoot, avoid homework, hop on bicycles to visit friends, construct tree houses, build slides constructed of ropes and wood slung between trees, and play in hedges.

Inside the house, where beautiful carpets and paintings gave the rooms their individuality, and Dainty Bess and Duftwolke roses, placed loosely in glass containers, filled the house with fragrance, my father often fussed around us in flurries of gentle and ineffectual scolding, which we generally ignored and interpreted as his way of paying us attention. I saw him angry only once in a lifetime and then he spoke very quietly and we were silenced with shock. Someone (who?) had been discourteous to a domestic. His voice turned cold as he said: "One may be impolite to someone in a superior position, but never . . . never to a subordinate, because such a person has no defence against you."

As we grew older we were included in the comfortable and gentle exchange of ideas on world and domestic affairs and about art and politics between my father and mother. New ideas were welcomed, but a delving into emotions was not encouraged. My mother talked about inconsequential things to us and her friends and said with confidence that talk should in many instances be like the chattering of birds and have no deeper meaning and that there were certain things which one should pretend did not happen in your life. Silences should not last. Conversation should be made.

Years later, when my father died on a cruise of the Mediterranean, my mother flew back and returned to us stunned, without crying a single tear about the husband she had lived for and adored all her adult life. "I don't want to be consoled," she said. "I want to be like an African woman, I want to sit in a corner, put a blanket over my head and grieve." She could not speak about her grief and shortly afterwards the person that she had been disappeared. She first became vague and then completely senile. We were dismayed, angry and deeply saddened in turns.

Quite a few years later, shortly after a heart-rending funeral, I scolded her and said, "Mom, you cannot forget about the death of one of your grandchildren, it is too terrible and too important to forget."

She turned to me and said with great clarity, "Do not make me go into places in my mind where I do not want to be," after which she immediately withdrew again into vagueness and senility.

116

She continued to be unable to speak about my father. But a series of small strokes plagued her as she grew into her deep eighties, and when they racked her she would yearningly call out to him and for him. The blanket over her head could not keep out the grief and the sad places in her head could not be avoided.

I, who am in the middle of two generations of humane people, am humbled now by my children's understanding of our sadness and their efforts to care for us and to protect us against the grinding knowledge of the daily harshness of their battle to lead meaningful lives. Malcolm, who is often surrounded by friends, remains humorous and light-hearted against all the endless odds. Marguerite, supported by the ever-interesting and thoughtful Ben, works determinedly, in her friendly and delicate way, to find various means of moving around without encumbering others. Frances remains the joyful, busy younger sister who brings much fun and activity into the house.

Our three children's courage has kept us more or less whole throughout the last few years and many old friends and family members have been around us like a shield and have talked us through years of uncertainty about how to keep this fragile family from falling apart. I love them all for doing this with humour and intelligence and caring.

They have always been the right people at the right place at the right time. When Marguerite's leg had been broken in a car accident I stood next to her bed and knew that my desperately sad-looking young daughter would have huge difficulties in coping with this further setback, with moving out of the depression which was settling over her and with continuing with her studies. My friend Lesley happened to be studying psychology with her at the time. The two of us conspired and (lying guiltily!) assured Marguerite that it seemed to us the simplest thing in the world for her to take a wheelchair and to go back to university to attend classes. The full force of the two of us planning lifts and ways and means of getting around campus, and our assurance that we could not even understand why she was worried by the prospect, had the desired effect and, a week or two afterwards, slightly stunned by having been swayed by the pair of us, Marguerite went back to university.

My Marguerite child – ever busy, practical and incisive – and I have had a running argument for many years because she assures me that I gain nothing from wanting to avoid sadness and hidden things. It is the secrets of life, especially those that one keeps from oneself, that cause and increase misery, she says. I am now astonished to find that it is my voice that tells Marguerite that certain parts of consciousness are called the inner life because that is their habitat: inside.

I don't want to be overwhelmed by sadness and have tried to keep our home running pleasantly, busily and filled with interesting conversation, but sadness catches up with me and when I teach, to my huge embarrassment, I cry about short stories and poems in front of classes full of astonished schoolchildren. Yet, when I look at my own children or think of the devastation being wreaked inside their bodies, I do not cry.

I see my children's different, miraculously strong characters and the way they live the lives that have been given to them – how they battle to move, to get out of bed, and how they nonetheless dance and teach from a wheelchair, study, swim, write and keep up with friends – and then I talk to them, argue with them, laugh with them, but, through years of training, I do not cry, not even now when it might do us all the world of good.

The years of training started when they were fifteen and thirteen. We had gone with Malcolm to many doctors through the years because of his strange gait and clumsiness. The verdict repeatedly came: "There is nothing wrong with him." The joy of the diagnosis would last a day, after which our gentle, amusing, intelligent child's strange movements would let us know that the process would be repeated in a few months' time. When the numbing words from the neurologist eventually came, a blanket never to be lifted covered our lives. Only once since then have I dreamt that nothing had happened, that nothing was wrong and in that dream Malcolm came running up to me laughing cheerfully. When I woke up immediately afterwards I felt light again with a lightness which I recognised but could hardly remember from many years before.

Marguerite was in grade 7. I sat waiting as children poured and pushed out of the school door. One of the thirteen-year-olds came out with two boys next to her. She looked up, sideways, at one of them, with her eyes half-closed and with a teasing smile on her lips. A knowledge of the new power of flirtation, which they all enjoyed, played over her sweet young face. After them Marguerite came out. As I looked at my lovely daughter I saw that her shoulders were asymmetrical, at exactly the same angle that Malcolm's were, and I knew that it would never be necessary to find a diagnosis for her. This knowledge seeped quietly, numbingly, blightingly into every cell of my body. "Hi, Mom," she said, and after having tossed her book bag into the back of the car she started talking happily about what had happened at school that day.

When is the right moment to tell a child that her life, like her brother's, would be different and immensely difficult – that after a short while she would be unable to walk? Of course I should have, but I never knew how to, never found the right time, and never did speak about it as she went right through secondary school: ever herself, ever busy with new and creative things . . . like the writing of

119

a play about District Six, where forced removals had in the sixties devastated a community.

This play, *Small Holdings*, was written on a wave of inspiration after she had read the poetry of Adam Small during the school holidays.

"I've asked the headmaster and he has agreed that it can be staged," she said, on day one of the new term.

"Oh?" I ventured tentatively, "That's nice . . ." anticipating any amount of upheaval in our lives. True to form, Marguerite insisted with the immovability of a concrete wall that she, who had never even been in a play in her life, would also be the director of this play. Auditions, play practices and ideas about costumes, sets and backdrops filled her conversation.

"What do you mean, costumes, sets and backdrops?" I asked timidly.

Up to that point I had seen myself as an innocent bystander, but now I knew that I had unwittingly, seamlessly and, above all, helplessly, become stage manager as Marguerite's ambitions and visions grew.

"Yes," the confident reply came, "we need a backdrop with Table Mountain in the background and colourful labourers' cottages in the foreground, and white headscarves for the girls in Muslim roles, and minstrels' costumes for the singing parts, and . . ."

"It cannot be done," I said firmly but desperately. "Opening night is in two weeks' time. Minimalism, modern sets, a hint of a character – perhaps in a hat or a tie?" my suggestions faltered as I saw new ideas growing in her eyes.

"I'm at my wit's end," I confided to a colleague, as my lament about the impossibility of producing a backdrop to match my daughter's vision in a week and a half filled her office.

"You mean," she asked, "a backdrop of Table Mountain with labourers' cottages in the foreground? At my son's school they had an operetta last week with exactly such a backdrop. They won't mind lending it to you. I'll find out," she promised.

"Oh, white head scarves?" asked my neighbour. "I've got a huge roll of white fabric left over from my days in the rag trade, let's go look in the attic."

"Certainly," said the curator at the District Six Museum, "we've got just the thing to decorate your foyer," and came back with huge transparent photographs. "Hang it against the light and it will produce a fantastic effect."

"Thank you," I said politely, knowing that this could not be done as no nails could be hammered into the ceiling of the foyer of the school's theatre.

"Look," said my friend who came to help me with the decorations, "next to the lights in the foyer are hooks at exactly, but exactly, the right place to hang the photographs."

And I, of little faith, ran around hanging backdrops and photographs until Marguerite came in with her unsteady gait and cheerful smile, saying, "My friend Louise and I went to the Waterfront, to a restaurant where we met a group of minstrels who said that they would come to the school to sing at the concert and that we could certainly borrow their costumes."

"Oh, that's nice," I said humbly to the young girl who had had a vision and who never for a moment doubted that it would happen exactly as she saw it in her mind's eye.

This book is a gift to my loved ones. I want to thank them for keeping me alive:

I climbed a sycamore tree
so I could nest
in the branches
of abundant life
and see the
bluebird

Friedreich's ataxia

Friedreich's ataxia is an inherited, progressive disorder of the nervous system that affects balance, co-ordination, movement and sensation. The word "ataxia" means unsteadiness, and loss of co-ordination is usually the earliest symptom of the condition.

Someone with Friedreich's ataxia may have difficulty walking or running, or appear clumsy; and lack of control may affect the arms and the hands early on. Increased impairment of balance and movement eventually leads to loss of the ability to walk. Speech impairment also develops early in the disease. Difficulty in co-ordinating precise movements of the lips and tongue leads to slower speech that is difficult to understand.

Friedreich's is the most common inherited type of ataxia, and is caused by a genetic mutation that results in reduced levels of the protein frataxin which appears to regulate the amount of iron within a cell. Without frataxin, iron builds up in the cells and causes damage. The cells most affected are those that transmit sensory and movement signals via long fibres.

At this point, there is no known way to slow the progression of Friedreich's ataxia. Cardiac disease develops later on in most cases, and, on average, people with ataxia live for three to four decades after their diagnosis.

Acknowledgements

This book, being my story, would not have life without those who give meaning and wonder.

To my parents for the integral role that they have played in my life and in my writing. To my mother, you've always believed in me, giving me light, warmth and immeasurable inspiration and support in every way. To my father, for constantly encouraging me to be creative and to keep on writing. To my siblings, for travelling together on our lives' unpredictable road; and to Benjamin Roux for lovingly sharing so much of your life with me, for giving me incredible emotional support and insight – I will love you always. In memory of Martine Imminkhuizen, my late friend, who has shaped and always will shape my perspective on life, and for never failing to wear her Diesel jeans; to my grandparents, for leaving behind the wonderful legacy of the story of their lives. And to my dear cousins: laughing with Gerald de Jager, chatting to Rina Benz and Carine de Jager, playing guitar with the Marx sisters. Thanks also to Professor Joan Hambidge who assisted me initially by supervising my master's thesis in creative writing: I elaborated on the thesis to create this book. I would also like to mention a few other academics for their inspiration: André Brink, a source of great encouragement, Etienne van Heerden, for support along the way, Stephen Watson, John Higgins, Henning Snyman and Chris van der Merwe. Many of my friends have shared ideas and given me support: a huge thanks to Ina Roux, my second mother, Saul Roux who is another brother to me, Liesel Hibbert, Selma Kieck, Jeanne van Zyl, Lou Naudé, Marianne Roux, Lesley Palmer, Gail Wallace, Marie Naudé, Carine Phyffer, Corrie Williams, Melt van Schoor, Jacques du Toit, Roxanna Strong, Arend Nagel, Nicky Visser, Colette Ashton, Carl Garisch, Linda Duvenhage, André Roux (for all the wonderful holidays), Adriaan Myburgh, Charles Kieck, Jenny Hall, Surika Walters, Sylvia Xabadiya, Amélie Guyot, Michael Thorn, Michelle du Plessis and Louise Cook. Thank you to Human & Rousseau's dedicated team. And also to the Jerusalem thorn tree in our garden in Grahamstown.

Most important, I would like to express my gratitude to families who have supported me and my family throughout our lives: the Rouxs, the Kiecks, the Marxs, the Louws, the De Jagers, the Barries, the Halls, the McAllisters, the Haighs, the Krones, the Kerschbaumers, the Naudés, the van Zyls, the Bothas, the Imminkhuizens and numerous others.